the Amazing Maurice

and his Educated Rodents

Terry Pratchett

adapted by Stephen Briggs

OXFORD
UNIVERSITY PRESS

Great Clarendon Street, Oxford OX2 6DP

Oxford University Press is a department of the University of Oxford.
It furthers the University's objective of excellence in research,
scholarship, and education by publishing worldwide in

Oxford New York

Auckland Bangkok Buenos Aires Cape Town Chennai
Dar es Salaam Delhi Hong Kong Istanbul Karachi Kolkata
Kuala Lumpur Madrid Melbourne Mexico City Mumbai Nairobi
São Paulo Shanghai Taipei Tokyo Toronto

Oxford is a registered trade mark of Oxford University Press
in the UK and in certain other countries

British Library Cataloguing in Publication Data

Data available

ISBN 978 0 19 831494 3

20

Printed in Great Britain by CPI Group (UK) Ltd., Croydon CR0 4YY

Acknowledgements

Illustrations on page 126 by David Wyatt, copyright © David Wyatt 2001,
reproduced by permission of the artist c/o The Sarah Brown Agency.
Other illustrations by Peter Melnyczuk.

Text extract from *The Amazing Maurice and his Educated Rodents* by Terry
Pratchett, published by Doubleday, copyright © Terry Pratchett 2001,
reprinted by permission of The Random House Group Ltd.

The Publisher would like to thank Jenny Roberts for writing the
Activities section.

Although we have made every effort to trace and contact copyright holders
before publication this has not been possible in all cases. If notified, the
Publisher will rectify any errors or omissions at the earliest opportunity.

Contents

General Introduction

With a fresh, modern look, this classroom-friendly series boasts an exciting range of authors – from Pratchett to Chaucer – whose works have been expertly adapted by such well-known and popular writers as Philip Pullman and David Calcutt.

Many teachers use Oxford *Playscripts* to study the format, style, and structure of playscripts with their students; for speaking and listening assignments; to initiate discussion of relevant issues in class; to cover Drama as part of the curriculum; as an introduction to the novel of the same title; and to introduce the less able or willing to pre-1914 literature.

At the back of each Oxford *Playscript*, you will find a brand new Activity section, which not only addresses the points above, but also features close text analysis, and activities that provide support for underachieving readers and act as a springboard for personal writing.

Many schools will simply read through the play in class with no staging at all, and the Activity sections have been written with this in mind, with individual activities ranging from debates and designing campaign posters to writing extra scenes or converting parts of the original novels into playscript form.

For those of you, however, who do wish to take to the stage, we have included, where necessary, 'A Note on Staging' – a section dedicated to suggesting ways of staging the play, as well as examining the props and sets you may wish to use.

Above all, we hope you will enjoy using Oxford *Playscripts*, be it on the stage or in the classroom.

What the Adaptor Says

The Amazing Maurice is a fantasy book and fantasy is about more than wizards. *The Amazing Maurice*, for instance, is about rats that are intelligent. But it is also about the even more fantastic idea that humans are capable of intelligence as well. And surely the possibility that evil could be conquered through talking is more intriguing than the idea that it might be destroyed simply by throwing an expensive piece of jewellery into a volcano? In Pratchett's story, the rats go to war … but then justice is done and they make peace, which is astonishing.

Of course, Pratchett is a humorous writer too, and humour has its uses. Laughter can get through the keyhole while seriousness is still hammering on the door. New ideas can ride in on the back of a joke, old ideas can be given an added edge.

British author G. K. Chesterton (1874–1936) famously defended fairy stories against those who said such tales told children that monsters exist, arguing that children already know there are monsters and that fairy stories simply teach them that monsters can be defeated. And, of course, we now know that the monsters may not simply have scales and sleep under a mountain: they may be in our own heads, in our ability as humans to create situations or machines of destruction.

In fact, if we look at the world around us, it is not hard to find examples of the way in which we humans can turn to violence if we feel threatened. But Terry Pratchett wouldn't insult even rats by turning them into mere metaphors and *The Amazing Maurice* shouldn't simply be read with a particular international situation in mind.

Of course, as a writer of humorous fantasy, Pratchett is often thought by newspapers to be obsessed by 'wacky', 'zany' ideas. One is that rats might be able to talk. And sometimes, when he's really, really wacky and on a fresh dose of zane, he's even capable of putting forward the fantastic idea that, in certain circumstances, humans might actually be capable of thinking. After all, it must be worth a go – we've tried everything else!

Stephen Briggs

A Note on Staging

Adaptor's Introduction

I have tried, in adapting *The Amazing Maurice*, to keep the staging as simple as possible. I know that some schools and colleges will have large budgets, or enthusiastic art departments, and will want to recreate the world in which the story is set. Many others, though, will manage with a few lighting changes and with cardboard cut-out rats' heads worn by black-clad actors, or will simply read the play in the classroom with no staging at all. It should work each way. The main thing is to keep the action flowing – don't let it get bogged down by complicated scene changes.

The Outsized Props

While many of the props you may need for a production of this play are normal in size – e.g. Doppelpunkt's trombone, Keith's flute – there are others which are 'outsized', larger than life. This is because they are used by rats who are, of course, a great deal smaller than humans!

The props that need to be 'outsized' are listed for you below, next to the name of the rat that uses them.

Peaches: the book, 'Mr Bunnsy Has An Adventure'; the pencil; the broken knife blade; the matches

Bitesize: the candle stub

Nourishing: the string

Sardines: the rubber bands

Feedsfour: the matches

The Play at a Glance

The outline of the play below highlights the props or scenery you may want to consider for a performance. These are in addition to the props particular to each character as outlined in the character list on pages 10 and 11 and the note on outsized props above.

Throughout

To one side of the stage there should ideally be a lectern – though you could easily improvise with a simple chair or table. It is from this position that Peaches, as though she is in church, reads each extract from 'Mr Bunnsy', illuminated by a spotlight.

ACT ONE

Scene One *A country road*
No special staging required.

Scene Two *Bad Blintz, the town square*
A doorway; a queue of people; pieces of paper (ration tickets); loaves of bread; sign on wall ('Rats Wanted Dead! 50 pence per tail! Apply to the Rat-catchers c/o the Rathaus').

Scene Three *The cellars below Bad Blintz*
No special staging required.

Scene Four *Malicia's house, the kitchen*
A table; a couple of chairs; a large Welsh dresser; a saucepan; some food and bits of crockery/cutlery (in this scene, Malicia prepares food for Keith and Maurice).

Scene Five *The tunnels under the town*
No special staging required.

Scene Six *The hayloft*
No special staging required.

Scene Seven *The tunnels under the town*
No special staging required.

Scene Eight *The hayloft, then the exterior of the rat-catchers' shed*

A sign depicting a Rat King – the sign of the ancient Guild of Rat-catchers. Note: For this scene, the set needs to take into account both the hayloft and the rat-catchers' hut. The characters move across the stage from one to another, with no change of scene to allow for a change in props or set.

Scene Nine *The tunnels under the town*
No special staging required.

Scene Ten *The rat-catchers' shed, interior*
Rats' 'skins'; piles of old traps; dog muzzles; wire netting; dust; tins on a shelf with labels that read 'Danger: Hydrogen Dioxide!',

'RatBane', 'FireGut', 'Polyputaketlon: Extreme Caution!', and 'Sugar'; a rat hole.

Scene Eleven *A room in the rat-catchers' shed*
One cage (to hold Hamnpork). In this scene, we hear the noise of hundred of scared rats in cages – this could involve the whole class 'squeaking' (possibly via a recording) or be symbolized through the use of discordant music to enhance the horror of the scene.

Scene Twelve *The sewers*
No special staging required.

Scene Thirteen *The tunnels under the town*
No special staging required.

Scene Fourteen *A cellar*
No special staging required.

ACT TWO

Scene One *A radio studio*
A desk; two chairs.

Scene Two *The tunnels under the town*
No special staging required.

Scene Three *The rat-catchers' shed, interior*
Two mugs; a spoon; a kettle; a pot labelled 'sugar'; an empty poison bag labelled 'Killalot'.

Scene Four *A pipe, interior*
A piece of paper (the Clan's rules, for Maurice to pick up); Peaches' outsized copy of 'Mr Bunnsy Has An Adventure'.
Note: In this scene, Maurice examines his conscience. Maurice's Conscience should be played by a male voice (offstage), possibly pre-recorded.

Scene Five *The tunnels under the town*
No special staging required.

Scene Six *The lair of the Rat King*
Note: During this scene, the Rat King makes its first appearance.

This may be achieved by lights coming up on him, or by his being discovered by opening a curtain – whatever will look most effective … and dramatic!

If you have decided to stage the Rat King using several individual 'rats' with their tails knotted together, you may wish these actors to deliver the Rat King's lines in unison. Alternatively, the Rat King's speech might be pre-recorded, or spoken into a microphone offstage by other cast members.

Scene Seven *The lair of the Rat King*
No special staging required.

Scene Eight *Bad Blintz, the Town Square*
No special staging required.

Scene Nine *The Mayor's office, interior; a country road*
A large meeting table; approximately 10 chairs; a large chest. Note: For this scene, the set needs to take into account both the interior of the Mayor's office and an 'outside' area (in which Maurice bids farewell to the town). One way of staging this might be to drop the curtain before Maurice's final speech, leaving Maurice alone at the front of the stage.

Characters

Rats

Dangerous Beans	(male) a 'little albino rat; very clever; nearly blind
Hamnpork	(male) head rat; 'big and fierce and a bit scabby'; doesn't like the idea of thinking; opposed to change; old
Peaches	(female) a young rat; drags 'Mr Bunnsy Has An Adventure'; carries a bag, containing a grubby piece of paper, a pencil, a broken knife blade, and some matches
Delicious	(male or female) one of the younger rats; rather nervous
Bitesize	(male or female) carries a candle stub
Rat King	(male or female) 'a group of rats with their tails tied together'; it is said that a Rat King can control other rats
a **Keekee**	an ordinary rat (i.e. non-speaking)★
Mr Clicky	a clockwork rat★
Rat	(male or female)
Other Rat	(male or female)
the **Rat King's rats**	(male or female)★

Number One platoon: Trap Disposal Squad

Darktan	(male) a natural leader; wears a belt which holds a sword, other tools, and a scrap of paper (a map)
Nourishing	(female) young, nervous, and eager; carries a quantity of string
Inbrine	(male) **Darktan's** efficient Deputy
Specialoffer	(male) a young rat

plus **various unnamed rats** (male or female)★

Number Two platoon: in charge of 'the cheeky stuff'

Sardines	(male) wears a straw hat; carries a walking stick and knapsack containing rubber bands; always 'tippity-tapping' with his feet

plus **various unnamed rats** (male or female)★

Number Three platoon: Widdlers

Feedsfour	(male) a young rat; carries matches
Kidney	(male or female) a small rat
Fresh	(male) deceased*
Rats 1-4	(male or female; if there is a shortage of actors, **Kidney** and **Feedsfour** could take the roles of **Rat 1** and **Rat 2**)

Humans

Keith	a 'stupid-looking' boy; carries a cap and flute
Malicia	the **Mayor's** daughter; well-dressed; carries a large bag containing hairpins and cotton wool
Ron and Bill	rat-catchers; unpleasant men; each carries a variety of traps and a big bag containing fake rat tails
Sally and Gary	radio commentators, with microphones and headsets
Mayor	wears an official-looking hat and robe
Doppelpunkt	a police sergeant; owns a trombone
Rat Piper	(male) carries a pipe
Rat Piper's Agent	an old man; carries a notebook
2 Councillors	(male or female)
Boy	carries a stick with a bundle tied to the end

plus **various unnamed people** (male or female)*

Other Characters

Maurice	(male) an ex-alley cat; self-appointed 'freelance negotiator'; gets more 'scruffy-looking' and dirtier as the play progresses
Death	(male) wears a black robe; carries a large scythe; very bony face
Maurice's Conscience	(male) an offstage voice

Notes

Older rats are 'scarred and bitten and ragged'
All rats carry between them a variety of packs and bundles

* These are non-speaking parts.

ACT 1

SCENE 1

A country road. **Maurice** *enters.*

Maurice

Good evening. This is a story about people and rats. The difficult part is deciding who are the people, and who are the rats.

Me? I am the Amazing Maurice. How did I get to be amazing? Well, it just happened. It was a while back, just after lunch one day. I looked at my reflection in a puddle and thought '*that's me*'. I mean, not 'hey, there's a cat' but 'that is me'. I knew I wasn't like other cats. Then I found I could talk. I was smart. And suddenly I knew that, in the real world, the smart thing is to be rich. Money is the key to everything. And then I found the educated rats. They could talk, too. And think. I'd always thought rats were stupid but suddenly they were clever. Some of them. Some of them could even read. The first book they read got them very excited. It told of a world they wanted to live in. A world with talking animals. A world where animals lived together in peace and harmony. The book became their *inspiration*. It was called 'Mr Bunnsy Has An Adventure'.

Peaches enters and walks into a spotlight. She is carrying a book – it is 'Mr Bunnsy Has An Adventure'. She opens the book and reads.

Peaches

[*Reading reverently*] Mr Bunnsy Has An Adventure. One day, when he was naughty, Mr Bunnsy looked over the hedge into Farmer Fred's field and saw that it was full of fresh green lettuces. Mr Bunnsy, however, was not full of lettuces. This did not seem fair.

Peaches exits. The light comes up again on **Maurice**.

Maurice

And then, one morning, soon after I found the educated rodents, I saw this stupid-looking kid playing the flute with his cap in front of him for pennies and I had an idea. An amazing idea. Rats, flute, stupid-looking kid …

Keith enters, carrying his flute.

Keith	Maurice?
Maurice	Yes, kid?
Keith	You don't think what we're doing is, you know ... *dishonest*, do you?
Maurice	How do you mean?
Keith	Well, we take people's money.
Maurice	And *who* do we take money from, exactly?
Keith	Well, usually it's the mayor, or the city council, or someone like that.
Maurice	Right. And that means it's ... what? I've told you this bit before.
Keith	Government money.
Maurice	Right! And what do governments do with money?
Keith	Er ...
Maurice	They pay soldiers. They have wars. In fact we've probably stopped a lot of wars by taking the money and putting it where it can't do any harm.
Keith	Some of those towns looked pretty poor, Maurice.
Maurice	Hey – just the kind of places that don't need wars, then.
Keith	Dangerous Beans says it's ... un-eth-ickle.

Peaches enters. She is carrying a bag containing an outsized stub of pencil and paper, and the outsized copy of 'Mr Bunnsy'.

Peaches	That's right, Maurice. Ahem. Dangerous Beans says we shouldn't live by trickery.
Maurice	Listen, Peaches, *trickery* is what humans are all about. They're so keen on tricking one another all the time that they elect governments to do it for them. We give them value

for money. They get a horrible plague of rats *[he indicates* **Peaches***]*. They pay a rat piper *[he indicates* **Keith***]*. The rats all follow the kid out of town, hoppity-skip, end of plague, everyone's happy that no one's widdling in the flour any more, the government gets re-elected by a grateful population, general celebration all round. Money *well* spent, in my opinion.

Peaches   But there's only a plague because we make them think there is.

Peaches and Keith exit. Maurice comes to the front of the stage again.

Maurice   I never meant to be amazing. It just happened. And then there were the rats. I knew there was something educated about the rats when I jumped on one and it said 'Can we talk about this?'. Then I realized you can't eat someone who can talk. At least, not until you hear what they've got to say.

The rats spent a lot of time worrying about *why* they were suddenly so clever. Waste of time, in my view. But the rats went on and on about whether it was something they'd eaten off the rubbish heap behind the wizards' college in Ankh-Morpork. All that discarded magical clutter and those enchanted chicken giblets. But that wouldn't explain how *I* got Changed because *I* don't eat stuff off rubbish heaps.

Keith enters with a crowd of rats. They include **Peaches, Dangerous Beans, Hamnpork,** *and others.* **Maurice** *points out front.*

What's the name of that town, kid?

Keith	*[Looking at a guide book]* It's called Bad Blintz *[pronouncing 'Bad' to rhyme with 'glad']*.
Peaches	Why is it bad?
Maurice	It doesn't mean it's bad – it's foreign for 'bath', see. And it's pronounced 'bart'. Bart Blintz. Bath Blintz. Because … well, because they got a bath, see? Very backward place, this. You probably have to buy tickets just to see it.
Dangerous Beans	Is that *true*, Maurice?
Maurice	*[To the audience]* Dangerous Beans. He's very difficult to deal with. He's virtually blind, but he sees a lot better than many of the others in some ways. *[To Dangerous Beans]* Anyway, it's a nice-looking town. Looks rich to me.
Peaches	Ahem.
Maurice	*[Sharply]* Yes?
Peaches	Do we *really* need to keep on doing this?
Maurice	*[With heavy irony]* Well, of course, *no*. I don't have to be here at *all*. I'm a *cat*, right? A cat with talents. People *like* cats. But, owing to being incredibly, you know, *stupid* and *kind-hearted*, I decided to help a bunch of rodents who are, and let's be frank here, not exactly number one favourites with humans. Now some of you *[he looks at Dangerous Beans]* have some idea of going to some island somewhere and starting up a rat civilization, which is very admirable, but for that you need … ?
Dangerous Beans	Money, Maurice, but –
Maurice	Money. Right. Sheesh, I just don't know what you lot would do without … anyone? Begins with an M.
Dangerous Beans	You, Maurice. But, you see, what we really think is –
Maurice	Yes?

Peaches	Ahem. *[Maurice groans]* What Dangerous Beans means is that all this stealing grains and cheese and gnawing holes in walls is, well, it's *not morally right*.
Maurice	But it's what rats do!
Dangerous Beans	But we feel we shouldn't. We should be making our own way in the world.
Maurice	Oh dear, oh dear, oh dear. Ho for the island, eh?

*He leans forward and taps **Peaches'** copy of 'Mr Bunnsy'.*

	The Kingdom of the Rats. Not that I'm laughing at your dream. Everyone needs their little dreams. *[Aside, to the audience]* If you know people's dreams, you can control them.
Peaches	Ahem. We think this should be the last time. This must be the very last time we do the silly plague of rats trick. And that's final.
Maurice	And what does Hamnpork think about this?
Hamnpork	What do you mean, think?
Peaches	*[Nervously]* I … sir, I think we should stop doing this trick.
Hamnpork	Oh, *you* think, do you? Everyone's thinking these days. I think there's a good deal too much of this thinking, that's what I think. I don't like this thinking. In my day, a leader just had to be big and stroppy. Everything's moving too fast. I don't like it. I thought we were going to get on a boat and find an island somewhere. Very ratty places, boats. And people tell me that now we have all this money and we can do all this *thinking*, we've got to be eff … efit …
Dangerous Beans	Ethical, sir.
Hamnpork	Which sounds *un*ratty to me.
Peaches	We already have lots of money, sir. More than we thought, isn't that right, Maurice? Because you said that gold coins were all shiny like the moon and silver coins were all shiny like the sun, but in fact it's the other way around, isn't it Maurice?

Pause. **Maurice** *looks somewhat embarrassed at being caught out.*

Dangerous Beans	So we think, sir, that after this one last time we should share out the money and go our separate ways. We should stop before it's too late. There's a river near here – we should be able to get to the sea.
Hamnpork	An island with no humans *or cats* would be a good place!
Maurice	What about you, kid?
Keith	I don't mind.
Maurice	Don't mind what?
Keith	Don't mind anything, really. Just so long as no one stops me playing. But maybe the rats are right. We've had a couple of narrow squeaks, Maurice.
Maurice	OK. Fine. We'll do it one more time and then split the money three ways. Fine. *Not* a problem. But if this is going to be the last time, let's make it one to remember, eh? Happy with that, kid?
Keith	I can go on playing my flute afterwards?
Maurice	Absolutely.
Keith	OK.
Maurice	[*To the rats*] So – I want to see maximum squeaking and making faces at people and widdling on stuff, OK?
Dangerous Beans	We think the widdling on stuff is not really –
Peaches	Ahem.
Dangerous Beans	Oh, I suppose, if it's the last time …
Hamnpork	I've widdled on everything since I was out of the nest. *Now* they tell me it's not right. If that's what *thinking* means, I'm glad I don't do any.
Maurice	Let's leave them *amazed.* Rats? They think they've seen rats in this town? After they've seen *us*, they'll make up *stories!*

Lights out. **Peaches** *comes to the lectern.*

Peaches [Reading] Mr Bunnsy had a lot of friends in Furry Bottom. But what Mr Bunnsy was friendly with more than anything else was food.

Peaches *exits.*

● ●

SCENE 2

The town square of **Bad Blintz**. **Maurice** *enters a spotlight and speaks to the audience.*

Maurice So – what is the plan? Everyone knows about plagues of rats. There are famous stories about rat pipers who made their living going from town to town getting rid of plagues of rats.

And that, really, is it. You don't need *many* rats for a plague, see? Not if they know their business. One rat, popping up here and there, squeaking loudly, taking a bath in the fresh cream and widdling in the flour, could be a plague all by himself.

After a few days of that, you'd be amazed how glad people are to see that stupid-looking kid and his 'magical' rat pipe. And they're amazed when rats pour out of every hole to follow him out of town.

Of course, they'd be really amazed if they found out that the rats and the piper meet up with a cat somewhere outside the town and count out the money.

RATIONING
QUEUE
HERE
FOR BREAD

*Lights come up on a street scene. People are walking to and fro, some are in a queue for food, by a doorway guarded by **Sergeant Doppelpunkt**. People go in with a piece of paper and come out with a loaf of bread.*

This isn't right. There should be fat women selling chickens and people selling sweets for kids, and ribbons.

Keith	There's nothing like that. There's hardly anything to buy, by the look of it. I thought you said this was a rich town, Maurice.
Maurice	Well, it *looked* rich.
Keith	*[Seeing a sign on a wall]* What's this? *[Reading]* Rats Wanted Dead! 50 pence per tail! Apply to the Rat-catchers care of the Rathaus *[pronouncing it to rhyme with 'bat house']*.
Maurice	They must *really* want to get rid of their rats here. I *told* you this would be the big one!
Keith	What's a 'Rathaus'? It can't be a house for rats, can it?
Maurice	It's just the local word for … the town hall. Nothing to do with rats. See that queue? People queueing for bread. Food is scarce. They're having to ration it out. Looks like they'll be needing a rat piper any day now. That's a watchman on the door. I don't like watchmen. That looks like *government* to me.

*The two **rat-catchers** enter. One is carrying a couple of bundles of fake rat tails. He accidentally drops a bundle as he passes **Maurice** and **Keith**, then both men go to speak to someone in the queue.*

Keith	Rat tails! They really must have a problem here!
Maurice	*[Looking at the dropped bundle of 'tails']* Bigger than you think. These tails look very odd to me. Just pick those up while no one's looking will you?
	Keith goes to pick them up, but the rat-catchers see him and cross to join them.
Ron	Now don't you go touching them, young sir. You can get the plague, you know, from rats. Makes your legs explode.
Bill	That's right, young sir, and then your brains come down your nose.
Ron	My colleague has put his finger right on it.
Bill	Which is more than you'd be able to do, because when you get the plague, your fingers go all –
Keith	*Your* legs haven't exploded.
Ron	Well said, young sir. But that's because lesson one at the Rat-catchers' Guild is not letting your legs explode.
Bill	*[Chuckling]* Which is a good thing, because the second lesson's upstairs.
Ron	Ain't seen you before, young sir. My advice to you is keep your nose clean and don't say nothing to nobody about nothing. Understand?
	Keith goes to open his mouth, then stops.
	Ah, you catch on quick, young sir.
Bill	I bet you'd like to be a rat-catcher when you grow up, young sir.
Ron	*[Leaning in so that his nose almost touches Keith's]* *If* you grow up, young sir.
	The rat-catchers exit. Malicia, who has just come out of the Rathaus, stands and looks at Keith and Maurice.
Maurice	Very unusual rat-catchers they have round here.
Keith	They looked *nasty*. Like they enjoy it.

Maurice	I haven't seen rat-catchers who've been so busy but who've still got clean boots. But even that's not as odd as the rats they have round here.
Keith	What's odd about the rats?
Maurice	They have very strange tails.
	Pause.
	Something's going on, and that means someone's getting rich, and when someone's getting rich, I don't see why that shouldn't be m—*us*.
Keith	But we don't want Dangerous Beans and the others getting caught and killed.
Maurice	They won't get caught. Those men wouldn't win any prizes for thinking. Even ordinary rats can out-think humans. Humans think that just because they're bigger, they're better …
	*He stops as **Malicia** crosses to them.*
Malicia	*[To **Keith**]* You're new here, aren't you? Come looking for work, have you? Probably got sacked from your last job, I expect. Probably because you fell asleep and things got spoiled. Or you ran away because your master beat you with a big stick. But you probably deserved it because of being lazy. And then you probably stole the cat, knowing how much people would pay for a cat round here. And you must have gone mad with hunger because you were talking to the cat and everyone knows cats can't talk.
Maurice	Can't say a single word.
Malicia	And probably you're a mysterious boy who – did that cat just say something?
Keith	I thought everyone knew that cats can't talk.
Malicia	Ah, but maybe you were apprenticed to a wizard. Yes, that sounds about right. But you fell asleep and let the cauldron of bubbling green stuff boil over and he threatened to, to turn you into a, a, a –

Maurice	Gerbil.
Malicia	A gerbil, and you stole his magical cat because you hated it so much and – did that *cat* just say 'gerbil'?
Keith	Don't ask me, I'm just standing here!
Malicia	All right. And then you brought the cat here because you know there's a terrible famine and that's why you were going to sell it.
Keith	But he's not much of a ratter.
Malicia	Ratter? Everyone's hungry here – there's at least two meals on that cat!
Maurice	*What?* You *eat* cats here?
Malicia	*[Triumphantly, prodding* Maurice *on the nose]* Got you! You fell for a very simple trick! I think you two had better come with me, don't you? Or I'll scream. And people *listen* to me when I'm screaming!
	They exit as the lights go out. Peaches *walks to the lectern.*
Peaches	*[Reading]* 'Never go into the Dark Wood, my friend' said Ratty Rupert. 'There are bad things in there.'
	Peaches *exits.*

● ●

SCENE 3

The cellars below Bad Blintz. Dangerous Beans, Peaches, Hamnpork, *and some other rats enter.* Darktan *is at the back of the crowd, as yet unseen.*

Dangerous Beans	All right, who's got the matches?
Feedsfour	*[Producing an outsized match]* Me, Dangerous Beans. Feedsfour.
Dangerous Beans	And who's got the candle?
Bitesize	*[Dragging an outsized candle stub]* Me, sir. I'm Bitesize.
Dangerous Beans	Well done, young rat. Put it down and Peaches will light it.

Peaches lights the candle and the rats gather round it.

Hamnpork	Can you really see it?
Dangerous Beans	Yes, sir. I am not completely blind. I can tell the difference between light and dark.
Hamnpork	I don't like it. We managed in the dark before. Besides, setting fire to a candle is a waste of perfectly good food.
Dangerous Beans	We have to be able to control the fire, sir. It shows we are not just rats.
Peaches	The younger rats say the shadows frighten them.
Hamnpork	Why? They're not frightened of complete darkness, are they! Darkness is ratty!
Peaches	We didn't know the shadows were there until we had the light.
Delicious	Um … and even when the light has gone out, we know the shadows are still all around.
Dangerous Beans	Well … Delicious?
Delicious	Yes, sir.
Dangerous Beans	Well, Delicious, being afraid of shadows is all part of us becoming more intelligent, I think. It shows your mind is working out that there's a you and there's also everything that's *outside you*. So now you're not just afraid of the things you can actually see and hear and smell, but also of the things you can … sort of … *see* inside your head. Learning to face the shadows outside helps us to fight the shadows *inside*. And you can control *all* the darkness. It's a big step forward. Well done.
Hamnpork	I don't see the point, myself. We did all right on the wizards' dump. And I was never scared of anything.
Dangerous Beans	We were prey to every stray cat and hungry dog, sir.
Hamnpork	Oh well, if you want to talk about cats –
Dangerous Beans	I think we can trust Maurice, sir. Not with money, perhaps. But he is very good at not eating animals who talk. He checks, every time. I believe he remains a decent cat at heart.

23

Peaches	Ahem. That remains to be seen. But now we're here, let's get organized.
Hamnpork	Who are you to say 'let's get organized'? Are you the leader, young female? It's *my* job to say 'let's get organized'.
Peaches	*[Meekly]* Yes, sir. How would you like us to get organized, sir?
	Pause.
Hamnpork	*[He hasn't a clue]* Just … get organized. Don't bother me with details! I am the leader.
	He stalks off.
Dangerous Beans	This is an ideal base. It smells secret and safe. A perfect place for rats.
Darktan	*[Moving forward]* Right. And you know what's worrying me about that?
Dangerous Beans	What is worrying you, Darktan?
Darktan	It's a perfect place for rats but there *aren't* any rats here. Except us. Rat tunnels, yes. But no rats at all. A town like this should be full of them.
Peaches	Oh, they're probably scared of us.
Darktan	Maybe. But things don't smell right. Thinking is a great invention, but we were given noses and it pays to listen to them. Be extra careful.
	He turns to the others.
	OK troops! You know the drill! Plague rats, in your platoons, in front of me *now!*
	The rats all form up into three groups.
	Very nice. Right! This is tricky territory troops, so we're going to be careful.
	He turns to a group.
	All right, Number Three Platoon, you're on widdling duty. Go and have a good drink.

Feedsfour	Oooh, we're *always* on widdling duty!
Darktan	*[Crossly]* That's cos you're good at it, my lad! Your mother *raised* you to be a widdler, so off you go and do what comes naturally! Nothing puts humans off like seeing that rats have been there before, if you catch my meaning! Do some gnawing as well. And run around under the floorboards and squeak! And no one goes in until they get the all-clear from the trap squad. Off you go, drink some water! Hup! Hup! Hup! One two one two one two …

The first group jog off.

	Number Two Platoon, you know the drill. I want to see lots of cheeky stuff. Stealing food out of cats' bowls, pies from under cooks' noses –
Sardines	False teeth from out of old men's mouths –
Darktan	*[Grinning]* That was a fluke, Sardines. I bet you can't do it again. *[To the others]* Anyway – if I don't hear ladies screaming and running out of their kitchens within ten minutes, I'll know you're not the rats I think you are. Well? Why are you all standing around? Get on with it! And … Sardines?
Sardines	Yes, boss?
Darktan	Easy on the tap dancing this time, all right?
Sardines	*[Doing a step or two]* I just got these dancing feet, boss!
Darktan	And no going on ahead of the trap squad!
Sardines	*[As he and the rest of the platoon exit]* Aw, boss, can't we have *any* fun?

*They go. **Darktan** turns to the last squad.*

Darktan	OK, Trap Disposal Squad, you know it all by now. Just remember this is a new town so we don't know what we're going to find. There'll be new types of traps, but we learn fast, don't we? Poisons, too. Never rush, never run. We don't want to be like the first rat, do we?
The Squad	No, Darktan!

Darktan	I *said*, what rat don't we want to be like?
The Squad	We don't want to be like the first rat!
Darktan	Right! What rat *do* we want to be like?
The Squad	The second rat, Darktan!
Darktan	Right! And why do we want to be like the second rat?
The Squad	Because the second rat gets the cheese, Darktan!
Nourishing	Er … sir?
Darktan	Yes, what's your name … miss?
Nourishing	Er … Nourishing, sir. Er … can I ask a question, sir?
Darktan	You're new, aren't you?
Nourishing	Yes, sir! Transferred from the Light Widdlers, sir!
Darktan	Ah, they thought you'd be good at trap disposal, did they?
Nourishing	Er … not really, sir. They said I couldn't be any worse than I am at widdling, sir.
	The squad laugh.
Darktan	How can a rat not be good at that?
Nourishing	It's just so … so … *so embarrassing*, sir.
Darktan	All right. What's your question?
Nourishing	Er … you said the second rat gets the cheese, sir?
Darktan	That's right. Remember that.
Nourishing	Yes, sir. I will, sir. But what does the first rat get?
Darktan	Good question, Nourishing. Squad! What does the *first* rat get?
The Squad	The Trap!
Darktan	And don't you forget it! Take 'em out, Specialoffer. I'll be with you in a minute.
Specialoffer	Let's go rats! Hut, hut, hut …

They jog off. **Darktan** *turns to* **Dangerous Beans**.

Darktan	That's got us started. If we can't get the humans looking for a good rat-catcher by tomorrow, we don't know our business.
Peaches	We need to stay longer than that. Some of our ladies are going to have their babies.
Darktan	We don't know it's safe here yet. Nature has to take its course, obviously. But we haven't explored. There *must* be other rats here. I know they keep out of our way, but even so. I'm going to join my squad. What's up with Hamnpork?
Peaches	He's … thinking about things.
Darktan	Thinking. Right. Well, I've got traps to see to. Smell you later!
	He exits.
Dangerous Beans	What is the matter with Hamnpork?
Peaches	He's getting old. He needs to rest a lot. He won't admit it, though. And I think he's worried that Darktan or one of the others is going to challenge him.
Dangerous Beans	Will they, do you think?
Peaches	Darktan's too wrapped up in breaking traps and testing poisons.
Dangerous Beans	I've been thinking that we shouldn't kill other rats. I should like you to write that down. What else have you written?
	Peaches *pulls out a grubby sheet of paper and a pencil stub.*
Peaches	*[Reading]* In the Clan is Strength, We co-operate, or we die, Don't Widdle where you eat. *[Writing]* No Rat to Kill Another Rat. *[Looking up]* But supposing we have to?
Dangerous Beans	Then we have to. But we shouldn't. That's only four. There's one more.
Peaches	*[Reading]* We Are The Changelings. We Are Not Like Other Rats.
	Black out. **Peaches** *enters the spotlight.*

Peaches	*[Reading]* The important thing about adventures, thought Mr Bunnsy, was that they should not be so long as to make you miss mealtimes.
	Peaches exits.

● ●

SCENE 4

*The kitchen at **Malicia's** house. **Malicia, Keith,** and **Maurice** are onstage. **Malicia** is getting some food for **Keith** and **Maurice**.*

Malicia	My father is the mayor, you know.
Keith	He's the government?
Malicia	Funny way of putting it, but yes. The council make the laws, really. He just runs the place and argues with everyone. *He* says we shouldn't have any more rations than any other people – to show solidarity in these difficult times. But I think once you've *shown* solidarity, you should be allowed a little extra. In fact, I think we get a bit less than everyone else. Anyway. So – you're a magical cat, are you?
Maurice	That's right, magical.
Malicia	Probably belonged to a witch, I expect. Called Griselda or some such.
Maurice	Yeah, Griselda, right.
Malicia	Who lived in a gingerbread cottage in the forest, probably.
Maurice	Yeah, right. Only it was a crispbread cottage, cos she was slimming. Very healthy witch, Griselda.
Malicia	That's not how it should go!
Maurice	*[Quickly]* Sorry. I tell a lie. It was gingerbread, really.
Malicia	And she had big warts, I am sure.
Maurice	Oh yes. Er … what's *your* name, miss?
Malicia	Promise not to laugh?

Maurice	All right.
Malicia	It's … Malicia.
Maurice	Oh.
Malicia	Are you laughing?
Maurice	No, why should I? Sounds an ordinary enough name to me.
Malicia	*[To Keith]* And have *you* got a name? You're not the youngest son of a king, are you? If your name starts 'Prince', that's a definite clue.
Keith	I think it's Keith.
Maurice	You never said you had a name!
Keith	No one ever asked before.
Malicia	'Keith' is not a promising start. It doesn't hint of mystery. Are you sure it's your real name?
Keith	It's the one they gave me.
Malicia	Ah, that's more like it. You were stolen away at birth, I expect. You probably *are* the rightful king of some country, but they found someone who looked like you and did a swap. You were probably found on a doorstep.
Keith	I was, yes.
Malicia	See! I'm always right! There was probably a magic sword in the basket with you.
Keith	There was just me and a blanket, and a note.
Malicia	A note? What did it say?
Keith	19 pints and one strawberry yoghurt.
Malicia	Why nineteen pints of milk?
Keith	It was the door of the Guild of Musicians. Quite a large place.
Malicia	Abandoned orphan is good.
Keith	The Guild taught me music. I'm good at it, too.

Malicia	Mysterious orphan, strange talent, distressed upbringing – it's all shaping up. What kind of music do you play?
Keith	Kind? There aren't any kinds, there's just music. There's always music, if you listen.
Malicia	*[To Maurice]* Is he always like this?
Maurice	This is the most I've ever heard him say.
Malicia	I expect you're keen to know about me, but you're too polite to ask.
Maurice	Gosh, yes.
Malicia	Well, you won't be surprised to learn that I've got two dreadful step-sisters. And I have to do all the chores!
Maurice	Gosh, really!
Malicia	Well, most of the chores. Some of them, definitely. I have to clean up my own room, you know! It's *extremely* untidy!
Maurice	Gosh, really.
Malicia	*And* it's very nearly the smallest bedroom. There's practically no cupboards and I'm running out of bookshelf space!
Maurice	Gosh, really.
Malicia	And people are incredibly cruel to me. You will note that we're in a *kitchen*. And I'm the mayor's daughter. Should the daughter of a mayor be expected to wash up at least once a week? I think *not*!
Maurice	Gosh, really.
Malicia	And will you just look at the torn and bedraggled clothes I have to wear!

Maurice and Keith look. Her clothes look fine. She points to a bit of the hem.

Here, just here. I had to sew that back myself, you know!

Sardines enters upstage, dancing. Malicia hasn't seen him; Maurice has.

Maurice	Gosh, re –
Malicia	And on top of all this I'm the one that has to queue for the bread and sausages every day. And then the rats take everything.
	Malicia turns, and sees Sardines.
	There! A rat!
	She throws a saucepan at him. **Sardines** *dodges behind the dresser. There is a loud, metallic 'snap'.*
Malicia	Hah! That's one rat less, at any rate.
Maurice	It was Sardines.
Malicia	No, it was definitely a rat.
Maurice	He just called himself Sardines because he saw the name on a can and he thought it sounded cool.
Keith	He was a good rat.
Malicia	Are you mad? The only good rat is a dead rat!
Sardines	*[From behind the dresser]* Hello?
Malicia	It can't be alive! It's a huge trap!
Sardines	Anyone there? Only the stick is bending …
Malicia	Please tell me rats can't talk!
	Maurice has gone up and looked behind the dresser.
Maurice	He's got the trap jammed open with his cane! Quick, kid!
	Keith goes behind the dresser. There are some metallic noises, and then **Keith** *emerges with* **Sardines,** *who is carrying a broken cane.*
Keith	Are you all right?
Sardines	Well, boss, all I can say is it's a good job rats don't wear underwear. Thanks, boss.
Malicia	OK. It goes like this. The rat is a magical rat. And he's not the only one. Something happened to them and now they're really

quite intelligent, despite the tap dancing. And they're friends with the cat … and they have an arrangement. Something to do with a plague of rats, right? All those towns we've heard about? Well, you go from town to town pretending to be a plague of rats and then thingy here –

Keith   Keith.

Malicia   Yes … he pretends to be a rat piper and you all follow him out. It's all a big swindle, yes?

Sardines   She's got us bang to rights, boss.

Malicia   Now – give me a good reason why I shouldn't call the Watch.

Maurice   If you do, you'll never find out how the story ends.

Malicia   It'll *end* with you going to *prison!*

Sardines   If we're finding things out, boss, there's something I'd like to find out.

Malicia   Well? And don't call me 'boss'!

Sardines   Why are there no rats in this city? There's rat runs everywhere and we've found a few dead ones, but we haven't found a living rat anywhere, guv.

Malicia   What do you mean? There's a *plague* of rats! *You're* a rat!

Sardines   Yes, but *we* only arrived this morning, guv.

Keith   *[Wearily]* You were right, miss. It is all a scam. I'm sorry we've been doing it. This was going to be the last time. You shared your food with us. We ought to be ashamed.

Malicia   So … when you come along with your trained rats –

Sardines   We prefer educated rodents, guv.

Malicia   All right, your educated rodents, and you move into a city, what happens to the rats that are there already?

Sardines   They keep out of our way, boss. I mean 'guv'.

Malicia   And there are no other rats here *at all?*

Sardines	No, guv. Few old skeletons.
Malicia	But the rat-catchers nail up loads of rat tails every day!
Maurice	Have you ever *looked* at those tails, miss?
Malicia	What do you mean?
Maurice	They're fake. Some of them, anyway. I noticed when they dropped some near us in the street. Do you know what an aglet is?
Malicia	Aglet? Aglet? What's an aglet got to do with anything?
Maurice	An aglet is that little metal bit on the end of shoelaces. Most of those tails are just old leather bootlaces. Ever looked closely at those rat tails?
Malicia	Of course not! You can get the plague from rats!
Maurice	Of course. Your legs explode. That's why you didn't see the aglets.
Malicia	*[The penny's dropping]* Ah – *ha*!
Maurice	So – you're not going to tell the Watch about us … ?
Malicia	What? That I've been talking to a rat and a cat? Of course not. They'll tell my father I've been telling stories again and I'll get locked out of my room.
Maurice	You get locked *out* of your room?
Malicia	Yes, it means I can't get at my books. I'm a special person, you know. My grandmother and great-aunt were Agonista and Eviscera Grim.
	Blank looks.
	The Sisters Grim? They wrote … fairy tales. Ones with lots of blood and bones and bats and rats in. I've inherited their story-telling talent.
Maurice	I kinda thought you had.

Malicia	And if there's no rats under the town and the rat-catchers are nailing up bootlaces, then I smell a rat.
Sardines	Sorry – I think that was me.
Malicia	Quick! Go out across the back yard and hide yourselves in the hayloft over the stables! I'll bring you some food. I know exactly how this sort of thing goes!

Black out. **Peaches** *walks to the lectern.*

Peaches	*[Reading]* Ratty Rupert was the bravest rat that ever was. Everyone in Furry Bottom said so.

Peaches exits.

• •

SCENE 5

The tunnels under the town. The **Trap Disposal Squad** *are onstage.* **Darktan** *is offstage when the scene starts. The onstage rats are peering off to where* **Darktan,** *unseen, is examining a trap.*

Darktan	*[Off]* I'm right over the cheese. Not been touched. Pretty old, too.
Inbrine	Careful, sir.
Darktan	*[Off]* Just as I thought. It's a Prattle and Johnson 'Little Snapper'. One of the old Mark Threes, but with the extra safety catch.
Nourishing	Oh, they're easy!

Darktan enters.

Darktan	Ah, Nourishing. Easy, is it? Glad to hear it. You can show us how it's done, then.
Nourishing	Er … when I said it's easy … I mean, Inbrine showed me on the practice trap and he said –
Darktan	No need to be modest. *I'll* just watch, shall I?
Nourishing	But, but, but –
Darktan	I'll tell you what. I'll work on the trap, shall I?

He exits. **Nourishing** *looks relieved.*

And you can tell me *exactly* what to do.

Nourishing	Er …
Darktan	*[Off]* Now, where was I? Oh yes. Here's a bar and a little spring and a catch. What shall I do now, Miss Nourishing?
Nourishing	Er … er … er …
Darktan	*[Off]* Things are *creaking* here, Miss Nourishing.
Nourishing	Er, er, you wedge the thingy …
Darktan	*[Off]* Which one is the thingy, Miss Nourishing? Maybe it's this –

There is a loud snap offstage.

Argh! Argh! Argh!

Nourishing *faints.* **Darktan** *enters.*

All fixed and quite safe.

He helps **Nourishing** *up.*

It's very important in the trap business to be definite, you see. You're definite or you're dead. The second rat gets the cheese.

He pulls out a map.

I'm a rat of action, but these *[he holds up the map]* are useful. If I draw pictures of a tunnel layout, the paper remembers. It doesn't get confused by new smells. Other rats can use it to see in their heads what the writer saw. Amazing stuff. Now, Inbrine – did you deal with this poison marked two tunnels back?

Inbrine	Buried and widdled on. It was the grey No. 2 Poison, too.
Darktan	Good rat. That's nasty eating.
Inbrine	We found trays of No. 1 and No. 3, too. Lots of them, with dead keekees all around.
Nourishing	Keekees?

Darktan	*Ordinary* rats. Important safety tip – don't eat a dead rat unless you know what it died of. Otherwise you'll die of it, too.
Inbrine	Dangerous Beans thinks we shouldn't eat rats at all. Not even keekees.
Darktan	Yeah, well, maybe. But you have to be practical out in the tunnels. Never let good food go to waste.
	*A rat, **Kidney**, rushes in.*
Kidney	Kidney, sir, No. 3 Heavy Widdlers. We've found a trap, sir! Not like the usual sort! Fresh walked right into it! Please come!
Darktan	Right!
	They exit. Lights black out.

• •

SCENE 6

*The hayloft. A moment, then a **keekee** enters, running. As it is about to exit, **Maurice** enters and grabs it.*

Keekee	Squeak!
Maurice	OK. Here's the deal. You just have to say something. Anything. 'Let me go', for example.
Keekee	Squeak!
Maurice	Fair enough. He kills it and drags it off into a corner.
	***Keith** enters.*
	It couldn't talk.
Keith	I didn't ask.
Maurice	I gave it a chance. You heard me, right?
	A scream, off, and the sound of broken crockery.
	Sounds like the lads are still working hard.
	Three loud knocks. Pause. Three more loud knocks. Pause. Three loud knocks again. Pause.

Malicia	*[Off]* Are you two up there or not?
Keith	Yes.
Malicia	*[Entering]* Didn't you hear the secret knock?
Maurice	It didn't sound like a secret knock.
Malicia	It *is* a secret knock! And you're supposed to give the secret knock in return!
Maurice	But if it's just someone knocking on the door in, you know, general high spirits, and we knock back, what are they going to think is up here? An extremely heavy beetle?
Malicia	*[After a pause]* Good point, good point. I know, I'll shout 'It's me, Malicia!' and *then* give the secret knock, and that way you'll know it's me and you can give the secret knock back. OK?
Keith	*[Innocently]* Why don't we just say 'Hello, we're up here'?
Malicia	Don't you have any sense of drama? Look, there've been a lot of complaints about the rats. My father's gone off to the Rathaus *[pronounced to rhyme with 'smart house']* to talk to the council. They've sent for the rat-catchers, Blunkett and Spears. You know what that means, don't you?
Maurice	Let's pretend we don't.
Malicia	It means we can break into their shed and solve the mystery of the bootlace tails! Of course, it would be better if we were four children and a dog, but we'll make do. Come on!
	Malicia exits.
Maurice	She's gone in the head, if you ask me. She doesn't live in the real world. Dangerous Beans is a bit like that. Highly dangerous, in my opinion.
Keith	He's a very kind and thoughtful rat!
Maurice	Yes, but the trouble is, see, that he thinks everyone else is like him. People like that are bad news, kid. And our lady friend, *she* thinks life works like a fairy tale.

Keith	Well, that's harmless, isn't it?
Maurice	Yeah, but in fairy tales, when someone dies … it's just a word.

Black out.

● ●

SCENE 7

*Back in the tunnels. The body of **Fresh**, in the trap, is in the 'fourth wall' (i.e. out towards the audience). The **No. 3 Heavy Widdlers** stand looking at the 'body'.*

Rat 1	Poor old Fresh. He was a good rat.
Rat 2	Should've looked where he was going, though. Let's get him out of the trap, then. Doesn't seem right, leaving him there.
Rat 1	Especially since we're hungry.
Rat 3	Dangerous Beans says we shouldn't eat rat at all.
Rat 2	What do you think happens to you, after you're dead?
Rat 1	You get eaten. Or you go all dried up, or mouldy.
Rat 2	But what about the bit inside?
Rat 4	The squishy green wobbly bit? You shouldn't eat that. Tastes *awful*.
Rat 2	No – I meant the bit inside you that's *you*. Where does *that* go?
Rat 4	Sorry – you've lost me there …
Rat 2	Well … you know, like … dreams. You know, when you wake up, where does the dreaming part *go*? When you die, where does that bit that's inside you go?
Rat 1	What, the green wobbly bit?
Rat 2	No! The bit that's behind your eyes!
Rat 4	You mean the pinky-grey bit?
Rat 2	*No* – the invisible bit!

Rat 4	How would I know? I've never seen an invisible bit! I don't like this kind of talk – it reminds me of the shadows in the candlelight!
Rat 3	They say the Bone Rat comes and gets you when you're dead, they say.
Rat 1	They say, they say. They *say* there's a Big Rat Underground who made everything. They *say* if you've been a good rat, maybe the Big Rat has got this tunnel full of good eating that the Bone Rat will take you to –

Darktan enters, with Nourishing.

Darktan	All right, all right, what's been happening? *[Seeing the 'body']* Ah. I see. What do I tell everyone?
Rat 1	Not to use tunnels that haven't been marked clear, sir. But Fresh never was a good listener.
Darktan	He's not going to be doing any more listening now, that's for sure. We've got to go. There are too many traps; too much poison. No one is to go any further along this tunnel, understood? Everyone say, 'Yes, Darktan'.
All Rats	Yes, Darktan!
Darktan	And one of you stand guard. *[Turning to Peaches]* Everyone's getting nervous. The fear is spreading – if the Changelings panic, they'll panic as normal rats.

He starts to leave.

Rat 2	What shall we do with Fresh, sir?
Darktan	*[Pausing, and speaking over his shoulder]* Don't eat the green wobbly bit.

Lights out. Peaches walks to the lectern.

Peaches	*[Reading]* There were big adventures and small adventures, Mr Bunnsy knew. You didn't get told what size they were going to be before you started. Sometimes you could have a big adventure even when you were standing still.

Peaches exits.

Back in the hayloft. **Keith** *and* **Maurice** *are onstage. We hear* **Malicia's** *voice.*

Malicia	Hello? Hello, it's *me*. I'm going to give the secret knock *now*!

She knocks three times.

Hello? Did you *hear* the secret knock?

Keith	Perhaps she'll go away if we keep quiet.
Maurice	I shouldn't think so. *[Calling out]* We're up here!
Malicia	You've still got to give the secret knock!
Maurice	Look, this me. OK? A cat that talks? How will you recognize me? Shall I wear a red carnation?

Malicia enters, crossly. She is carrying a large bag.

Malicia	I don't think you're a *proper* talking cat, anyway. You don't wear boots and a sword, or a hat with big feathers in it.
Maurice	Boots?
Malicia	It was in a picture book I read.
Maurice	I don't do clothes.
Malicia	Come on, it's nearly dark. We shall move like cats!
Maurice	I expect I can manage *that*.

They leave the barn and move around to the **rat-catchers'** *hut. They look at the sign by the door. It shows a sort of star made up of rats with all their tails tied in a big knot.*

Malicia	That's the sign of the ancient Guild of Rat-catchers.
Keith	I know. It looks horrible.
Maurice	The door's locked. Why does it need to be locked, if rats make your legs explode?
Malicia	Luckily, I'm prepared for every eventuality.

She delves into her huge bag.

Maurice	What have you got in there? *Everything?*
Malicia	The grappling hook and the rope ladder take up a lot of the room. And then there's the big medicine kit, and the small medicine kit, and the knife, and the other knife, and the mirror for sending signals and … these.

She pulls out a roll of black cloth containing hairpins.

Hairpins. To pick the lock. They always work in stories.

She applies one to the lock. There is a satisfying click.

Good.

She opens the door and goes in. We hear her voice.

Oh *no*. I didn't expect *this*.

• •

SCENE 9

*The tunnels. **Darktan, Hamnpork, Peaches,** and **Dangerous Beans** are onstage.*

Darktan	We've triggered all the traps we've found so far but there are still lots more traps and new poisons all over the place. There are lots of 'humane' traps, too. But no rats in them.
Dangerous Beans	Humane traps?
Hamnpork	I got caught in one once. Then a female human came along and tipped me out over the garden wall. Couldn't see the point of it.

Darktan	I believe that some humans do it to be kind but I don't think anyone's trying to be kind here. There's lots of rat smell, but no live rats. Where are they all? We have to find where the keekee rats have gone.
Hamnpork	I will lead the expedition! I'm the senior rat around here!
Darktan	Fine. Mr Clicky will be in front in any case.
Hamnpork	Mr Clicky?
Peaches	*[To Hamnpork]* It's a clockwork rat we send in to test dangerous traps. *[To Darktan]* I thought Mr Clicky got smashed last week?
Darktan	We still have two left. Then we'll have to raid another pet shop.
Hamnpork	*I'm* the leader, Darktan. *I'll* say what we do.
Darktan	Fine, sir, fine. And you know how to make all the traps safe, do you?
Hamnpork	No! But I can tell you to!
Darktan	*[Calmly]* Good. Good. And you'll tell me which levers to leave alone and which bits to wedge open, will you?
Hamnpork	*[Gruffly]* I don't have to understand about traps.
Darktan	But I do, sir. And there are things about these new traps I don't understand. And until I understand them I *respectfully* suggest you leave it all to me.
Hamnpork	That's not the way to talk to a superior rat!
Darktan	*[Bowing]* I am sorry. Impertinence was not intended.
Hamnpork	Well, er …
Darktan	Obviously, as the leader, you must give the orders.
Hamnpork	Yes, er …
Darktan	But my *advice*, sir, is that we investigate this. Unknown things are dangerous.

Hamnpork	Yes. Certainly. Yes, indeed. We will investigate. Of course. See to it. I am the leader, and that is what I am saying.
	Black out.

● ●

SCENE 10

	*Inside the **rat-catchers' shed**. **Malicia**, **Keith**, and **Maurice** are onstage. **Malicia** is deeply disappointed.*
Maurice	Well, it *looks* like a rat-catchers' shed – lots of rat skins hanging up, piles of old traps, dog muzzles, wire netting, a considerable amount of dusting not having been done …
Malicia	Exactly! This is too normal. I was expecting some ghastly clue as well.
Keith	Does there have to be a clue?
Malicia	Of course! Look, there's two types of people in the world – those who have got the plot and those that haven't.
Maurice	The world hasn't *got* a plot. Things just … happen, one after another.
Malicia	Only if you think of it like that. Look, there'll be a secret passage, of course. Everyone look for the entrance!
	They start looking around.
Keith	Er … how will we know it's the entrance to a secret passage? What does a secret passage *look* like?
Malicia	It won't *look* like one, of course!
Maurice	Oh *well*, in that case, I can see dozens of secret passages – doors, windows, that kettle …
Malicia	You're just being sarcastic.
Maurice	Actually, I was being flippant. But I can do sarcastic if you like.
Keith	*[Looking at tins on a shelf, and reading the labels]* Danger: Hydrogen Dioxide!, RatBane, FireGut, Polyputaketlon:

43

Extreme Caution!, Sugar. They keep the poison next to the sugar. So many poisons …

| Malicia | This isn't working. |

| Maurice | I suppose there might not *be* a secret passage? |

| Malicia | There *has* to be a secret passage. Otherwise there's no *point*! Of course! We're doing it all wrong! Everyone knows you never find the secret passage when you're *looking* for it! It's when you give up and lean against the wall that you inadvertently operate the secret switch! |

She leans nonchalantly against the wall. No click.

Probably the wrong place.

| Keith | I don't think you'll find it that way. |

He looks down at the skirting board.

Why is there a rat hole in a rat-catcher's shed?

He kneels to examine it.

| Malicia | At least I'm being *constructive* about things! |

| Keith | I wouldn't come near this place, if I was a rat. |

| Malicia | Yes … it's often the stupid person who comes up with the good idea by accident. |

*She crouches down by the hole. **Keith** moves slightly back against the wall.*

There's a sort of little lever in here. I'll give it a push …

*There is a clonk, part of the wall falls away just by **Keith**, and he falls out of sight.*

Oh yes. I thought something like that would probably happen.

Malicia looks through the hole into the cellar.

It's full of sacks!

| Keith | [*Off*] I'm not hurt much, thank you. All these sacks broke my fall. |

Malicia	*[Still looking through the hole]* And … there's strings of sausages … smoked meat! Bins of vegetables! It's *full* of food! *[Turning to Maurice]* We were told the rats had got it all. But it was the rat-catchers all along! And we paid them out of *our* taxes! Let's go and tell the town Watch, then it'll be a big cream tea for all of us and medals all round, and then –
Maurice	I'm suspicious.
Keith	*[Emerging from the hole]* Why?
Maurice	Because I'm a suspicious character! I wouldn't trust your rat-catchers if they told me the sky was blue.
Malicia	But they've been blaming the rats and then killing them all so there'd be more food for *them*. Very clever.
Maurice	That's what's puzzling. Frankly, your rat-catchers are not the brightest. Frankly, if it was raining meatballs they wouldn't be able to find a fork!
Keith	There was wire netting in the cellar, too.
Malicia	So? They probably use it to make cages.
Keith	Exactly. Why would rat-catchers put rats in cages? Dead rats don't run away! I may be stupid-looking, but I'm not stupid! I have time to think about things because I don't keep talking *all the time!* I look at things. I listen.
Malicia	I *don't* talk all the time!
	She sees something, off.
	A rat!
	Maurice leaps off into the wings.
Maurice	*[Off]* OK – just say one word and you're OK.
	There is a sharp smack, as of a stick hitting a cat's head.
Maurice	*[Off]* Ow!
	Enter Sardines, dusting himself off.

Sardines	Do you *mind?*
Maurice	*[Following him on, rubbing his nose]* Dere's bno deed to be like dab!
Sardines	I'm wearing a *hat!* Do you ever bother to look?
Maurice	All right, I'm sorry! Why're you here?
Sardines	Looking for you or the stupid-looking kid. Hamnpork sent me. You won't believe what we've found! You've ruined this hat, you know!
Maurice	I *did* ask if you could talk! I always ask! I'm very definite about asking, you know!
Sardines	Yes, yes, you've made your point. I believe you.
Maurice	I'd hate anyone to think I didn't ask.
Sardines	OK. Forget it. This is serious! We found this room, boss – it's *full* of caged rats! But the worst of it is, the rat-catchers came in while we were there! And they've captured Hamnpork! Come *on!*

The lights black out as they exit. **Peaches** *walks to the lectern.*

Peaches	*[Reading]* And because of Olly the Snake's trick with the road sign, Mr Bunnsy did not know that he had lost his way. He wasn't going to Howard the Stoat's tea party. He was heading into the Dark Wood.

Peaches exits.

SCENE 11

*Another room in the **rat-catchers'** shed. There is a noise of
hundreds of scared rats in cages. The only visible cage, to one side,
has a very angry **Hamnpork** in it. **Keith**, **Maurice**, **Malicia**, and
Sardines enter.*

Malicia	All these foul cages … And that smell …
Keith	*[Looking at the offstage cages]* Hundreds of rats! It's horrible!
Maurice	Can't you feel it? The pressure of all those terrified minds? Trying to get into your mind?
Keith	They're frightened out of their minds! This isn't a story! This is real – do you understand? Now, let's get Hamnpork out of here!
Maurice	Someone's coming! Hide!

*He and **Sardines** slip into a small hole. **Keith** and **Malicia** can't
follow. Before they can do anything, the **rat-catchers** enter.*

Ron	What're you doing here, miss?
Bill	Playing hide and seek?
Ron	You broke into our shed. That's called 'breaking in', that is.
Malicia	You've been stealing our food and blaming it on the rats! Why have you got all these rats caged up? And what about the aglets, eh? Didn't think we'd spot that, eh?
Ron	Aglets?

Keith	The bits on the ends of bootlaces.
Ron	You idiot, Bill! I *said* we had enough real ones! I *told* you someone would notice! Didn't I tell you someone would notice? Someone *noticed!*
Malicia	Ah … you are the Humorous Thugs. I see how this works – one big fat one, one thin one – so, who's the big boss?
Ron	You know what your father's been and gone and done? He's only been and gone and sent for the rat piper!
Bill	He costs a fortune! Three hundred dollars a town!
Maurice	*[Poking his head out of the hole, to the audience]* Three hundred? And we only charge thirty! I'm outta here!
Ron	*[To Keith]* It's *you*, isn't it? The stupid-looking kid! You turn up and suddenly there's all these new rats around! You and your funny-looking cat! If I see that cat again it's going to have *mittens!*
Bill	Hur, hur, hur.
Ron	And we don't have a boss.
Bill	Yeah – we're our own bosses.
Ron	And you, miss, are too lippy by half. *[Turning to Keith]* What's that? A penny whistle?
	He takes Keith's rat flute.
	Think you're a rat piper, do you?
	He snaps it in two and tosses it aside. Keith suddenly charges at Ron, but Ron easily knocks him to the ground.
Bill	*[Walking across to Hamnpork's cage]* Why don't we put him in with that new rat?
Ron	*[Also walking over to look at Hamnpork]* Yeah, he's not a local rat. Killed several of ours and took a chunk out of my finger. *[To Hamnpork]* You're a plucky little fighter, you are.
Keith	Kind of you to say so.

Ron	I was talking to this *rat*, kid. Go and tie these two up somewhere, OK?
	Bill moves them to the other side of the stage and ties them up, out of earshot.
	We'll put them in one of the other cellars for now.
Bill	But she's the mayor's daughter. Mayors can get really upset about daughters.
Ron	He'll do what he's told, right? Now then, this new rat – he's special, he is. *[Looking at Hamnpork again]* I've got a use for *you*, my lad.
Bill	*[Moving back to **Ron**]* Not the pit?
Ron	Yes, the pit.
Bill	Tonight?
Ron	Yes – cos Fancy Arthur is putting his terrier Jacko on a bet to kill a hundred rats in less than quarter of an hour.
Bill	He can do it, too. Jacko's a good terrier. He did ninety a few months back. Should be a good show.
Ron	So you'd bet on Jacko, then?
Bill	Sure. Everyone will.
Ron	Even with our fighting friend in there with the other rats? Full of spite and boiling bile?
Bill	Well, er …
Ron	Right.
Bill	I don't like leaving those kids here, though.
Ron	It's 'them kids' not 'those kids'. Get it right. Rule 27 of the Rat-catchers' Guild – 'Sound stupid'. People get suspicious of rat-catchers that talk too good.
Bill	Sorry.
Ron	Talk thick, *be* clever.

Bill	I forgot.
Ron	You tend to do it the other way around.
Bill	Sorry. Them kids. It's cruel, tying people up. Why don't we just hit 'em on the head and throw 'em in the sewer. They'll be miles down river before they gets fished out and they probably won't even be recognizable by the time the fishes have finished with 'em.
Ron	I 'ad no idea you was so kind-hearted, Bill.
Bill	*And* I've got an idea about gettin' rid of this piper, too …
Rat King	*[Off]* NO! We can use the piper!
Ron	*[Flatly]* No! We can use the piper!
Bill	*[Flatly]* That's right. I was just thinking the same thing.
	Pause.
	Er … *how* can we use the piper?
Rat King	*[Off]* Isn't it OBVIOUS?
Ron	*[Flatly]* Isn't it obvious?
	He starts to exit.
Bill	*[Following him]* Yeah, obvious. Obviously it's obvious. Er …
	They exit. Black out.

● ●

SCENE 12

*The sewers. The lights change to a single spot, into which **Maurice** now enters.*

Maurice	OK. I've waded through the sewers and I smell like a rat, but at least I'm still free.
Rat King	*[Off]* What kind of thing are you? I can't see you, I don't know what you are. Come closer. Come CLOSER!
Maurice	I'm happy where I am, thank you.

Rat King	*[Off]* Then will you share our pain?
	*Dramatic noise. **Maurice** winces, but the pain is not too bad.*
	What kind of creature are you? Your mind is all WRONG!
Maurice	I prefer amazing. Anyway – who are *you?*
	*A couple of the **Rat King's rats** enter, into the shadows just outside the spot.*
Rat King	*[Off]* Here come my rats. They are all my eyes … WHAT? You're a CAT! CAT! KILL! You see my followers, cat? Watch them come for you, CAT!
Maurice	'You see my followers'? 'You see them'? How do you know? Are you reading my mind? No! You're not, are you? You can't read my mind, but you *can* see what I see! You see through my eyes!
	He shuts his eyes.
Rat King	*[Off]* Open them!
Maurice	Shan't! You can't hear my thoughts! You only use my eyes and ears – you're just *guessing* what I'm thinking. And your rats can't find me because I don't smell of cat – I smell like the sewers! All I have to do is to *feel* my way out of here and *you* can't follow me!
	*Maurice exits as **Peaches** walks to the lectern.*
Peaches	*[Reading]* Mr Bunnsy realized that he was a fat rabbit in the Dark Wood and wished he wasn't a rabbit or, at least, not a fat one. But Ratty Rupert was on the way. Little did he know what was waiting for *him.*
	Peaches walks to her place in the next scene.

• •

SCENE 13

*The tunnels. **Peaches, Darktan,** and **Dangerous Beans** are onstage. **Maurice** enters, feeling his way.*

Peaches	It's Maurice.
Darktan	Smells better than he usually does.
Maurice	Oh, ha, ha.
Dangerous Beans	I knew you wouldn't let us down, old friend. Can you help us? We need a plan –
Maurice	I suggest we go upwards at every opportu –
Darktan	To rescue Hamnpork. We don't leave our people behind.
Maurice	We don't?
Darktan	*[Firmly]* We *don't!*
Peaches	And then there's the kid. Sardines told us he's tied up in a cellar with the female kid.
Maurice	Oh, well, *humans*. I don't think we should meddle. I know about humans, they'll sort it out –
Darktan	I don't care about humans, but those rat-catchers took Hamnpork off in a cage! You saw that room, cat! Full of cages! It's the *rat-catchers* who've been stealing the food. And there's something else …
Maurice	A voice.
Darktan	*You* heard it? I thought it was just us!
Maurice	The rat-catchers can hear it, too. Only they think it's their own thoughts.
Dangerous Beans	It's frightened a lot of the other rats – they've just stopped thinking. How can that happen?
Darktan	It seemed to affect some of us more than others. We've got to get Hamnpork. He's the leader. We're rats, after all. A clan. Rats will always follow the leader.
Maurice	But he's a bit old, and you're the tough one, and he's not exactly the brains of the outfit …
Darktan	He's one of us! They took him away! They're rat-catchers! He's one of us! Are you going to help or not?

Maurice	*[Hurriedly]* Yeah, help you. Yeah, yeah.
Peaches	Ahem. Do you really *mean* that, Maurice?
Maurice	Yeah, yeah. Right.
Darktan	Sardines is following the rat-catchers to see where they're taking Hamnpork.
Maurice	I've got a bad feeling I already know.
Peaches	How?
Maurice	I'm a cat, right? I was in a barn once, up in the hayloft. Hunting for r—er, hunting for food. These men came in with lots of dogs and they put up this big round wooden wall in the middle of the floor. And there were men with boxes of rats and they tipped the rats into this ring and then they put some dogs in, too. Terriers.
Darktan	The rats fought the dogs?
Maurice	Well, I suppose they *could* have done. They mostly ran around and around. They call it rat coursing. Rat-catchers bring the rats. That's what'll happen to Hamnpork.
Darktan	Rat coursing. Why haven't we heard of it?
Maurice	Why would you hear about it?
Darktan	Surely one of the rats who –
Maurice	*None* of the rats come out alive. That's why you've never heard of it.
Peaches	Can't they jump out?
Maurice	Too high.
Darktan	Why don't they *fight* the dogs?
Maurice	Because they're *rats*, Darktan! Lots of rats, panicking. You *know* how it happens. One rat can think and be brave but a bunch of rats is just a mob – an animal with lots of legs and no brain.
Peaches	That's not true! Together we are strong!

53

Darktan	Exactly *how* high is this wall?
Maurice	Humans were leaning their elbows on it. Why? It's far too high for a rat to jump, I know that!
Peaches	Everything we've achieved we've done by working together.
Darktan	We'll rescue Hamnpork together, then. Look – it's Sardines and Nourishing.

Sardines and Nourishing enter. Nourishing is carrying a roll of string.

What's happening, Sardines?

Sardines	They've gone to a stables on the far side of town. Lots of dogs around. Men, too. You can get a good view from the beams over the wooden ring on the floor of the barn.
Maurice	Rat pit. Told you.
Darktan	Right. We're going to get Hamnpork out of there. Sardines will show me the way. The rest of you should try to find the kid.
Peaches	Why are *you* giving orders?
Darktan	Because someone has to. We need to rescue Hamnpork. He might be a bit scabby but he *is* the leader.
Sardines	Can Nourishing come with us, sir? She's carrying the string. Useful stuff, string.
Darktan	All right – but she'd better be able to keep up. Could you drop into the pit on a string?
Sardines	I'm game for anything, guv.
Nourishing	Into a pit with dogs in it? And wouldn't the string cut you in half?
Sardines	Ah – I've got something which helps, there.

He pulls out a coil of rubber bands.

Bands of rubber. I pinched them off a desk when I was looking for string. I've used 'em before, boss. Very handy for a long drop.

Darktan	Good. Because I'm getting an idea. If this plan of mine doesn't work, though, you're to use this.
	*He pulls out a match and gives it to **Nourishing**.*
	I want them to remember tonight. But I'm confident. This is what I thought: if you can drop down …
	***Darktan, Nourishing,** and **Sardines** exit. **Darktan's** voice fades as they leave the stage.*
	We should be able to grab Hamnpork …
Dangerous Beans	One rat can be brave, but a bunch of rats is a mob. Is that right, Maurice?
Maurice	No, I was … look, there was *something* back there! It's in a cellar. I don't know what it is. It's the voice that gets into people's heads!
Peaches	Not everyone. It didn't frighten you, did it? Or us. Or Darktan. Why?
Rat King	*[Off]* I will find a way in, CAT!
Maurice	Did you hear that?
Peaches	I didn't hear anything.
Dangerous Beans	*[Staring at 'Mr Bunnsy Has An Adventure']* I hoped it would be better than this. But it turns out we're just rats. As soon as there's trouble, we're just … rats.
Maurice	If it's any help, I'm just a cat.
Dangerous Beans	But you are not. I sense that, deep down, you have a generous nature.
Peaches	At least you ask people before you eat them.
Maurice	*[With a groan, looking guilty]* Um. I've been meaning to talk to you about that.
Peaches	Yes?
Maurice	Well … you know I always *do* check my food these days …

Dangerous Beans	Yes, and it does you great credit.
Maurice	*[With another groan]* Well, you know we've always wondered how I got changed even though I never ate any of that magical stuff you rats ate off the wizards' rubbish dump …
Peaches	Yes. That's always puzzled me.
Maurice	*[Shifting uneasily]* Well, er … did you ever know a rat, quite big, one ear missing, bit of white fur on one side, couldn't run too fast cos of a bad leg?
Peaches	That sounds like Additives.
Dangerous Beans	Oh yes. He disappeared before we met you, Maurice. A good rat. Had a bit of a speech difficulty.
Maurice	*[Gloomily]* Speech difficulty?
Peaches	He stammered. Couldn't get his words out very easily.
Maurice	*[Hollow-voiced]* Not very easily.
Dangerous Beans	I'm sure you never met him, Maurice. *[Wistfully]* I miss him. A wonderful rat.
Peaches	*Ahem. Did* you meet him, Maurice?
Maurice	*[In a rush of conscience]* All right! I ate him, okay? I was just a cat! I hadn't learned to think yet! I didn't know! I was hungry! Cats eat rats – that's how it goes! And *he'd* been eating the magic stuff and I ate him so then I got Changed too. I didn't know he was anyone! I didn't know I was anyone! On dark nights I think I can hear him talking to me! I admit it! I ate him! It wasn't my faaullltt!
Peaches	*[After a pause]* Yes, but that was a long time ago, wasn't it?
Dangerous Beans	Are you sorry for what you did?
Maurice	Sorry? What do *you* think? Sometimes I have nightmares where I burp and he –
Dangerous Beans	Then that's probably all right.
Maurice	All right? How can it be all right? You know the worst part?

I'm a cat! Cats don't go round feeling *sorry!* Or guilty!

Dangerous Beans *[Miserably]* We don't behave how rats are supposed to behave either.

Peaches Shall I read to you from 'Mr Bunnsy'? That always cheers you up.

Dangerous Beans shakes his head.

Maurice *[To himself]* I'm a cat. I ought to just run off and leave you to ...

Peaches What is it, Maurice?

Maurice *[With a heavy heart]* We'd better see what's happened to the kid. Come on.

Black out.

● ●

SCENE 14

A cellar. **Keith** *and* **Malicia** *are tied up onstage.*

Malicia So – let's go over this again ... You don't have a knife of any kind?

Keith That's right.

Malicia Or some handy matches that could burn through the rope?

Keith No.

Malicia And no sharp edges near you that you could rub the rope on?

Keith No.

Malicia And you can't sort of pull your legs through your arms so that you can get your arms in front of you?

Keith No.

Malicia No super powers?

Keith No! Look, I'm just a normal person. Yes, all right, I was abandoned as a baby. It just happened. It doesn't make you special. I don't have any amazing powers. OK, I'm good at

57

playing quite a few musical instruments. But I'm the kind of person heroes *aren't*. Understand?

Malicia	Oh. In fact, you can't be any help at all?
Keith	No.
Malicia	*[After a short pause]* You know, I don't think this adventure has been properly organized.
Keith	Malicia, don't you understand? This is *not* a story. Real life isn't a story. Do you understand?
Malicia	My granny and great-aunt were very famous story tellers, you know.
Keith	You said.
Malicia	I used to get beaten when I was small for telling stories.
Keith	Beaten?
Malicia	All right then, smacked. On the leg. But it *did* hurt. *[A new thought]* Aren't you interested in *anything* except music? He broke your flute!
Keith	I expect I'll buy another one.
Malicia	Well, I'll tell *you* something. If you don't turn your life into a story, you just become a part of someone *else's* story.
Keith	Sounds silly.
Malicia	Huh. Look at you. You're just a face in someone else's background. *You* let a cat make all the decisions!
Maurice	*[Off]* Would you like us to go away until you've stopped being human?
Keith	Maurice? Where are you?
Maurice	In a drain. And believe me, it has not been a good night. Peaches is bringing a candle in.
Malicia	Who's Peaches?
Keith	Another thinking rat – a Changeling.

Malicia	Like Pilchards?
Keith	Sardines.
Malicia	See? A story! The plucky rats rescue our heroes.
Keith	Oh, we're back in *your* story, are we?
	Scuffling, off.
Malicia	What are they doing?
Keith	Trying to light their candle. Dangerous Beans thinks light and shadow are very important.
Malicia	Dangerous Beans? What sort of name is that?
Keith	They just learned words off old food tins, and signs, and things. They didn't know what the words meant, they just liked the sounds.
	The candle is lit and **Peaches** *enters, carrying it, followed by* **Dangerous Beans** *and* **Maurice**.
	Peaches and Dangerous Beans – this is Malicia. Her father is the mayor here.
Dangerous Beans	Hello.
Peaches	Mayor? That's government! Maurice says governments steal from people.
Malicia	How did you teach them to speak?
Keith	They taught themselves. They're not trained animals, you know. *[To Peaches]* We'd like you to gnaw through our ropes, please.
Peaches	I've got a bit of broken knife blade. It's for sharpening the pencil. Would that be better?
	Peaches cuts their ropes.
Malicia	Knife? Pencil?
Keith	I did say they weren't ordinary rats.

Malicia	Yes, well, tell them I'm very grateful.
Keith	Tell them yourself.
Malicia	I'm sorry – I just find it a bit embarrassing – talking to rats. It's so … childish. So … tinkly-winkly. So … Mr Bunnsy.
Peaches	Mr Bunnsy?
Malicia	It's just some books that some stupid woman wrote. Stupid stuff for ickle kids. Rats and snakes in clothes, so nice and cosy it makes you sick.
Keith	I think you'd better stop.
Malicia	There's no sub-texts, no deaths, no social commentary. Pathetic!

Peaches and Dangerous Beans, upset, exit.

Keith	Oh boy. I never had the heart to tell them. They thought it was all true.
Malicia	In the Land of Furry Bottom, possibly.
Keith	You upset them. You're just no good at *listening*, are you? Not to *what* people say, or *how* they say it! There's something bad going on here. Much worse than men stealing food.

Keith and Malicia argue in silence as Maurice moves to the front of the stage to address the audience.

Maurice	Humans, eh? They think they're the lords of creation, but everyone knows cats are. Ever see a cat feed a human? Case proven.
Rat King	*[Off]* How the humans shout.
Maurice	Who *is* that? My conscience? Is that you, Additives?
Rat King	*[Off]* No – it is I. I am … SPIDER.
Maurice	You're a *spider?* I could take on a spider with three paws tied behind my back!
Rat King	*[Off]* Not *a* spider. SPIDER! Now I'm in your HEAD, cat. I'm in your HEAD and I will never go AWAY! I'll be in your DREAMS!

Maurice	*[Desperate]* Look, I'm just passing through. I'm not looking for trouble! Just let me get into the nice fresh air and I'll be right out of your ... hair, or legs, or whatever.
Rat King	*[Off]* You don't want to run AWAY.
Maurice	I don't want to run – hold on, I *do* want to run away! I'm a *cat!* No rat is going to control *me!* You've tried!
Rat King	*[Off]* Yes – but then you were STRONG. Now your little mind runs in circles and wants someone else to do the thinking for it. I can think for you. I can think for EVERYONE! I will always be with you. *[The voice fades away]* Always be with you ... Always ...
Maurice	*[Snapping out of it]* Right, time to say farewell to Bad Blintz. The party is *over.* The rats have got lots of other rats and even these humans have each other but I've just got me and I'd like to get me somewhere where strange voices don't talk to me. *[Moving back into the scene]* 'Scuse me, are we going or what?
Keith	What?
Maurice	I'd prefer going.
Keith	They've called in a rat piper, Maurice. And the clan is all over the place. A *real* rat piper, Maurice, not a fake like me. He'll be here in the morning. He'll have a magical pipe. Do you want to see that happen to our rats?
Maurice	Well, not exactly *see*, no.
Keith	Right. So we're not going to run away.
Malicia	So what are we going to do?
Keith	We're going to talk to the rat-catchers when they come back.
Malicia	And why will they want to talk to us?
Keith	Because ... if they don't talk to us, they're going to die.
	Black out.

SCENE 14

ACT 1

END OF ACT ONE

ACT 2

• •

SCENE 1

*Two **radio commentators** are sitting at a desk, with microphones in front of them.*

Sally Good evening listeners, and welcome to what promises to be an exciting evening of ratbaiting from the Red Barn in Bad Blintz. How is it looking to you, Gary?

Gary Well, Sally, there's quite a crowd here already and I can see the black top hats of the two rat-catchers moving through the crowd to the pit. And yes *[a crowd roar, off]* there goes the first sack of rats and the first terrier, too. It's Jacko – he's a dog with a lot of form, isn't he Sally?

Sally That's right, Gary.

Gary What a scene! Twenty rats all trying to find a corner to hide in in the wooden circle of the pit.

Noise (off) of cheering, jeering, rat squeals, and terriers barking.

Sally What a slaughter! The rats don't stand a chance!

Gary Wait! The rat-catchers are putting in another rat – he looks a really mean one!

Hamnpork *[Offstage, over the crowd noise]* Idiots! Work together! You could strip this fleabag to the bone!

Sally Who shouted that? I thought the rat did for a moment!

Hamnpork *[Off]* Now you'll find out how a *real* rat dies!

Sally It was! It was the rat! Has that happened before, Gary?

Gary *[Checking a sort of Wisden for ratbaiting]* Not as such, Sally. There was a bout in 1875 when one of the terriers was heard to say 'sausages', but nothing like this.

Sally Oh my God – I don't believe it! Another rat has dropped out of the rafters on a length of string! It's wearing a hat!

Twanging noise, off.

Gary	I wish you could see this, listeners … The rat in a hat has grabbed the big talking rat and twanged back up into the rafters!
Sally	And *another* rat's come out of the rafters! His weight pulled the other two up into the roof, I guess! He's dropped a lantern onto Jacko's head! He's bitten through his rope and landed in the ring! This is unbelievable!
Darktan	*[Off]* Right! Now I'm going to show you how a rat can *live!*
Sally	*He's* talking too! This is unbelievable!
Gary	I've never seen a rat like this before! He doesn't run like a rat should! He ducks like a fighter! Jacko doesn't know where to turn! The rat's attacking him from all sides!
Sally	Ten dollars on the rat, Gary?
Gary	*[Turning to her]* No bet, Sally!

A yelp offstage and a pained 'Oooh!' from the crowd, and from Sally, who is still watching the fight.

	What happened?
Sally	The rat's just bitten Jacko on the … well, on a part of Jacko that's a bit private! He looks distressed! He's trying to climb out of the ring!
Gary	I don't blame him! Look, what's this? The rat's climbed up Jacko's back and out of the ring!
Sally	He's gone! He's gone! Right through that hole and out of the barn! What a night, Gary!
Gary	What a night, Sally! Well, that must be it from Bad Blintz. Goodnight, listeners.
Sally	Goodnight.

*Black out. **Peaches** walks to the lectern.*

Peaches	[*Reading*] Farmer Fred opened his door and saw all the animals of Furry Bottom waiting for him. 'We can't find Mr Bunnsy or Ratty Rupert!' they cried.
	Peaches exits.

● ●

SCENE 2

*Follow spot on **Darktan**, as he makes his way along the tunnel.*

Darktan	That showed them! That showed them what a rat can do!
	*He exits. There is a loud 'snap' and a cry of pain from **Darktan**. A moment's pause, then **Nourishing** rushes on.*
Nourishing	Darktan? Darktan!
	*A groan from **Darktan**, off. **Nourishing** crosses to him and looks to where he lies, offstage.*
	You're caught in a trap!
Darktan	[*Off, forcing out some heavy sarcasm, despite the pain*] Oh ... really?
Nourishing	I'll go and fetch Sardines, shall I?
Darktan	[*Off, with effort*] No! Tell me ... what ... kind ... of ... trap?
Nourishing	Er ... er ... er ...
Darktan	[*Off*] *Think*, you miserable widdler!
Nourishing	Er, er, it's all rusty. Rust everywhere. Looks like it could be a Breakback – yes, there's a bit of the sign – it's a ... Nugent Brothers 'Breakback' Mark 1, sir!
Darktan	[*Off*] That's ancient, that is! Can you see how ... can ... you see how ... the spring, the spring ... So – this is now it

happens. Perhaps there really is a Big Rat, deep underground … The Bone Rat … nothing to fear … just walk into the light, Darktan … it's so easy …

Nourishing It's all rusted, sir!

She moves into the wing. There is a grinding sound.

[Off] I've gnawed through it, sir! It's old and weak!

*She comes on, helping **Darktan,** who has a red mark around his waist.*

Probably why you weren't cut in half, sir! Can you hear me, sir?

*She helps **Darktan** to the ground.*

Darktan *[Dreamily]* Quite nice, really. This must be where the Big Rat lives …

Nourishing Darktan, sir? I gnawed right through the spring, sir …

Darktan He must know a lot, the Big Rat.

He passes out.

Nourishing Sir? Sir? Are you still dead, sir? Sir?

*A small pause, and then **Darktan** breathes in, painfully and noisily.*

Nourishing It's amazing! You were dead in the trap and now you're alive!

Darktan Nourishing? I'm very grateful, but don't get silly. The spring was stretched and weak and the teeth were all rusted and blunt. That's all.

Nourishing But there's teeth marks all round you! No one's ever come out of a trap before!

Darktan I was just lucky.

Nourishing Did you see the Big Rat?

Darktan What? No, well, I'm not actually sure. There was a light and … is Hamnpork all right?

Nourishing	Sort of. I mean, we can't see any wounds that won't heal. He's had worse. But he was pretty old. Nearly three years.
Darktan	Was?
Nourishing	*Is* pretty old, I mean, sir. Sardines sent me back to find you because we need you to help us to get him back, but –
Darktan	I'm all right. I'm sure it looks nastier than it is. Let's get up there then, shall we?
	Black out.

● ●

SCENE 3

The rat-catchers' hut. The rat-catchers enter, crossly. Bill starts to make the tea.

Bill	You know where you said it was going to be such a good evening? Tell me about it again, cos I think I missed that part!
Ron	Shut up.
Bill	Someone punched me in the eye!
Ron	Shut up.
Bill	*And* I think I lost my wallet. That's twenty dollars I won't see again in a hurry!
Ron	Shut up.
Bill	And we left the dogs behind!
Ron	Shut up.
Bill	Do rats often whizz through the air like that? Or is that the kind of thing you only hear about when you are a *hexperienced* rat-catcher?
Ron	Did I say shut up?
Bill	Yes.
Ron	Shut up. All right, we'll leave. We'll take the money and nick a boat. We'll leave the stuff we haven't sold and we'll just *go*.

	I can smell things going bad.
Bill	Just like that?
Ron	Yes! Just like that! Time to move on! The jig is up, the bird has flown and the cat is out of the bag –
Maurice	*[Off]* I wish I was.
Ron	The – did you say something?
Bill	Me? No.
Ron	All right, then. It's been a long night. I don't want to be here when people come looking for us. People are going to ask questions and the only question I want them asking is 'where did the rat-catchers go?'. What's in the kitty?
Maurice	*[Off]* Kitty yourself.
Ron	What did you say?
Bill	Nothing. Cup of tea? You always feel better after a cup of tea.
Ron	Yeah. Three sugars.
Bill	*[Spooning it in]* That's right. Got to keep up your strength.
	He hands the tea to **Ron,** *who takes a swig at it.* **Bill** *adds three spoonfuls to his own mug.*
Ron	How did we get into all this? Stealin' stuff and blamin' it on the rats? Breeding big, tough rats for the rat pit? That's all fair enough, but I didn't used to be the sort of guy who ties up kids.
Bill	We made a big wadge of cash, though.
Ron	Yeah. There's that, I suppose. Is this new tea?
Bill	*[Taking a big swig at his]* No, just the usual.
Ron	Tastes a bit different. OK, let's get the –
Maurice	*[Off]* Now stand still and listen to me. If you run away, you'll die. If you talk too much, you'll die. If you wait too long, you'll die. Any questions?

ACT 2   SCENE 3

He walks in.

Ron	It's that kid's damn' mog!
Maurice	If I was you, I wouldn't look at me, I'd look at the rat poison.

They turn to the bench.

Bill	Here – who stole the poison?
Maurice	Steal it? We don't *steal*. That's *thieving!* We just put it somewhere else.
Ron	*[Realizing where the poison's gone]* Oh.
Bill	That's dangerous stuff! You tell me where it is right now!

Keith now enters, followed by Malicia. He carries an empty poison bag.

Ron	Oh dear.
Bill	What have you done with the poison?
Keith	Well … now that you mention it, I think I put most of it in the sugar.
Ron	*[Looking a bit poorly]* I *knew* that tea tasted funny …
Bill	*[Also looking poorly]* You nasty little –
Malicia	And don't even think of attacking us, or you'll never walk out of here alive. We might forget where we put the *antidote*.
Ron	What poison was it?
Keith	*[Sniffing the empty bag]* By the smell of it, the one the rats call 'Number Three'. The bag says 'Killalot'.
Bill	The *rats* call it 'Number Three'?
Keith	They know a lot about poison.
Bill	And they *told* you this … ?
Ron	We heard them talking, in the pit, remember? But there's *no* antidote to Killalot!
Keith	The rats found one.

Bill	*[Falling to his knees]* Please, young sir! Have mercy! If not for me, please think of my dear wife and my four lovely children who'll be without their Daddy!
Malicia	You're not married. You don't have any children!
Bill	I might want some one day!
Keith	What happened to that rat you took away?
Bill	Dunno, sir. A rat in a hat came out of the roof and grabbed it and flew away! And then *another* big rat came down into the pit, shouted at everyone, and bit Jacko on the … on the unutterables, and jumped right out of the pit and done a runner!
Keith	You stole from everyone and blamed the rats, didn't you?.
Bill	Yes! Yes, we done that!
Maurice	*[Quietly]* You killed the rats.
Bill	Yes, yes, that's right, we did!
Keith	*Why* did you do it?
Bill	Well, Ron said the rats ate the stuff *anyway*, so, he said if we got rid of all of the rats and pinched the stuff ourselves, well, it wouldn't exactly be like *stealing*, would it? More like … *re-arranging* stuff. There's a bloke Ron knows who comes up with a sailing barge in the middle of the night and pays us –
Ron	That's a lie!
Keith	But you caught rats alive and crammed them into cages without food. They lived on rat, those rats. Why did you do that?
Ron	*[Clutching his stomach]* I can feel things happening!
Keith	That's just your imagination – your stomach won't start to melt for at least twenty minutes!
Malicia	*[Impressed]* Wow!
Keith	And after that, if you blow your nose, your brain will … well, let's just say you'll need a *really big* handkerchief!

Malicia	This is great! I'm going to take notes!
Keith	And then, if you … well, just don't go to the lavatory, that's all.
Bill	This is inhuman!
Keith	No, it's very human. There isn't a beast in the world that'd do it to another living thing, but your poisons do it to rats every day. *Now tell me about the rats in the cages!*
Bill	See, rat-catchers have always caught rats alive for the pits. It's a perk. Nothing wrong with it! So we had to keep up a supply, so we bred 'em. And then …
Keith	Yes?
Bill	Ron said if we bred rats from the ones who survived the pits, we'd end up with bigger, better rats, see?
Malicia	What would be the point of that?
Bill	Well, miss, we – Ron said, we thought that … well, it's not exactly *cheating* to put really tough rats in amongst the others, see, especially if the dog that's going in is a bit borderline. Where's the harm in that? Give us an edge, see, when it come to betting. I thought … he thought …
Keith	You seem a bit confused about whose idea it was.
Both rat-catchers	His!
Rat King	*[Off]* Mine. What does not kill us makes us strong. The strongest breed.
Malicia	*[Not having heard the Rat King]* You mean … if we didn't have rat-catchers here we'd have *fewer* rats? No, there's something else. Something you haven't told us. Those rats in the cages are mad … insane.
Maurice	*[To the audience]* So would I be, with this voice in my head all the time!
Ron	I'm going to throw up, I really am!
Keith	Don't. You won't like it!

Maurice	*[To Keith]* I have to go. To find the others. Ask them what's in the other cellar.
	Maurice exits.
Keith	What is in the other cellar, then?
Bill	*[On the verge of telling them]* Only the ... only the ... that's where ... *[Changing his mind]* Can't say. There's nothing. Yes, that's it. Just old cages. Don't go in there, though, cos of the plague.
Malicia	He's lying. No antidote for *him*.
Bill	*[Suddenly confessing all]* I had to do it! You've gotta do one to join the Guild!
Ron	That's a Guild secret! We *don't* give away Guild secrets!
	He stops and grabs at his rumbling stomach.
Keith	What was it you had to do?
Bill	Make a rat king!
Keith	*[Sharply]* A rat *king?* What's a rat king?
Bill	I – I – I – stop it, I don't want to – we – I made a rat king – stop it, stop it – a rat king –
Malicia	And it's still alive?
Keith	*You* know about these things?
Malicia	Of course. There's lots of stories about them. Rat kings are deadly evil. They –
Bill	Antidote, antidote, *please!* My stomach feels like there're rats running around in it!
Malicia	You made a rat king. Oh dear. Well, we left the antidote in that little cellar you locked us up in. I should hurry, if I was you.
	Both men start to stagger quickly out.
Keith	Oh, I nearly forgot. There's only enough antidote for one person. But I'm sure you can work it out ... in a humane sort of way.

*He turns back to **Malicia**.*

What was it you really put in the sugar?

Malicia	Cascara.

Keith looks blank.

It's a laxative.

Keith still looks blank.

It makes you ... go.

Keith	Go where?
Malicia	Not *where*, stupid! You just ... go. I don't want to have to draw you a picture!
Keith	Oh. You mean ... *go*. And you just happened to have it on you?
Malicia	Of course. It was in the big medicine bag. It could easily be necessary.
Keith	How?
Malicia	Well, suppose we were kidnapped by pirates? They have a very monotonous diet. Or supposing we escaped and swam to a desert island and had to live on coconuts? Those things can be quite binding.
Keith	Yes, but ... *anything* can happen! If you think like that, you'd end up taking just about everything in case of just about anything!
Malicia	*[Calmly]* That's why it's such a big bag.
Keith	How much did you give them?
Malicia	Lots. But they should be all right if they don't take too much of the antidote.
Keith	Why, what's in the antidote?
Malicia	Cascara. Where's your cat?
Keith	Sometimes he just wanders off. And he's not my cat.

Malicia	Yes, you're his boy. But a young man and a smart cat can go a long way, you know.
Keith	How?
Malicia	Well, how about Dick Livingstone, who became Lord Mayor of Ubergurgl because his cat was so good at catching r— pigeons.
Keith	It was rats really, wasn't it?

Malicia nods.

	And it was just a story. Never mind stories about mayors. Are there really stories about rat kings?
Malicia	Rat kings have been around for years. Like on the sign outside.
Keith	What? A bunch of rats with their tails all tied together?
Malicia	Rat kings are deeply mysterious.
Keith	How do they get their tails tied together?
Malicia	The stories say it just happens. I read that their tails become stuck together in the nest, because of all the muck, and then get twisted up as –
Keith	That doesn't work. Rats generally have only six or seven babies, they have quite short tails, and the parents keep the nest quite clean.
Malicia	There's a preserved rat king in a big jar of alcohol in the town museum. It's ten rats, like a sort of star, with a big knot of tail in the middle.
Keith	That rat-catcher said he'd *made* one. He said he did it to get into the Guild. Do you know what a masterpiece is?
Malicia	Of course, it's anything really good …
Keith	A *real* masterpiece is something that a Guild apprentice makes at the end of his training to show the senior members of the Guild that he deserves to be a 'master'. Understand? It might be a great symphony, a beautiful piece of carving, a batch of first-class loaves – his 'master' piece.

Malicia	So?
Keith	So what sort of masterpiece would you have to make to become a master rat-catcher? To show that you could *really* control rats? It'd be very difficult to tie ten rats' tails together while they were alive – slippery bits of string that are moving all the time and the other end that keeps on biting you? Ten? Twenty? Thirty angry rats?
Malicia	Some of the stories about rat kings say they can control other rats. With their minds, sort of. Rat kings can't move around easily, so they learn how to see out of the eyes of other rats, and hear what they hear.
Keith	Just other rats?
Malicia	Well, one or two do say that they can do it to people.
Keith	But has it ever happened, *really?*
Rat King	*[Off]* YES.
Malicia	Yes, what?
Keith	I didn't say anything. You just said 'yes'.
Rat King	*[Off]* Silly little minds. Sooner or later there is always a way in. The cat is much better at resisting! You will OBEY me. Let the rats GO.
Malicia	*[Flatly]* I think we should let the rats go.
Keith	I was just thinking that.
Rat King	*[Off]* And forget about me. I am just a story.
Malicia	*[Flatly]* Personally, I think rat kings are really just a story. That rat-catcher was just a stupid little man. He was just babbling.
Keith	I wonder if we should *really* let the rats out? They looked pretty hungry. Ravenous. It could be very dangerous – they could attack us!
Malicia	They can't be worse than the rat-catchers, can they? Anyway, the piper will be here soon. He'll lead them to the river, or something …

Keith	Into the river …
Malicia	That's what he does …
Keith	Oh yes … *[Coming to slightly]* But rats can –
Rat King	*[Off]* Obey me! Don't THINK! Follow the story!
Malicia	Rats can what?
Keith	Rats can … rats can … I can't remember. Something about rats and rivers. Probably not important. Yes, let's release the rats …
	They move to the cages as the lights black out. **Peaches** *walks to the lectern.*
Peaches	*[Reading]* And as night fell, Mr Bunnsy remembered: there's something terrible in the Dark Wood.
	Peaches *exits.*

● ●

SCENE 4

In the pipe. **Maurice** *enters.*

Maurice	*[To the audience]* Why am I doing this?
His Conscience	*[A voice, off]* Because you're a kind person at heart.
Maurice	No, I'm not.
His Conscience	Actually, that's true. But we don't want to tell that to Dangerous Beans, do we? *He* thinks you're hero!
Maurice	Well, I'm not.
His Conscience	Then why are we scrabbling around underground to try to find him?
	Maurice *sees a piece of paper in the water in the pipe. He picks it up.*
Maurice	*[Reading]* No Rat to … We Are Not Like Other Rats. They wouldn't drop this, would they? Not the *Rules*. Peaches always carries it as if it's a hugely precious thing …

Rat King	*[Off]* Will I find them first? Or perhaps I already have … What strange things they are, CAT. Rats that think they are not rats.

Maurice groans and moves on. He sees something else in the water. Again, he fishes it out. It is the book.

Maurice	'Mr Bunnsy Has an Adventure'? They dropped 'Mr Bunnsy'? Were they running away? Or did they throw it away? No.
Rat King	*[Off]* Where are they now, CAT? Can you find them? Which way now?
Maurice	It can see what I see. It can't read my mind, but it can see what I see and hear what I hear and it's good at working out what I'm thinking. It can see what I see …

*He shuts his eyes. Behind him, some of the **Rat King's rats** enter.*

Rat King	*[Off]* In the dark, CAT? How will you fight my rats? The ones BEHIND YOU!

Maurice spins around.

Well done, CAT! You see the squeaky creatures and yet you don't leap! How did a cat learn not to be a cat?

*The rats move forward, together. **Maurice** takes a step back.*

Imagine a million clever rats. Rats that don't run. Rats that share one mind, one vision – MINE!

Maurice	Where are you?
Rat King	*[Off]* You will see me soon. Keep going, pussy cat. One word from me and these rats will take you down. You might kill one or two, but there will always be more. Keep going.

Maurice moves on, followed by the rats.

They are close, cat. Shall we play a game? Cats like playing. Did you play with Additives? BEFORE YOU BIT HIS HEAD OFF?

Maurice	You are going to *die*.
Rat King	*[Off]* They are getting closer to me, Maurice. So close now. I

have their feeble minds under my control! I can make them open up the rats' cages! They will do anything I say! Shall I tell you that the stupid-looking kid and the silly-sounding girl are going to DIE? Do you know that rats can eat a human ALIVE?

Black out.

● ●

*Underground. A candle is illuminating the area. **Hamnpork** is lying on the ground. **Darktan**, **Sardines**, **Nourishing**, and some other rats are gathered around.*

Sardines	Will he be all right, guv? What is it? Poison, guv?
Darktan	No, I think it was all just too much for him. Just too much.
Hamnpork	Am … I … still … the … leader?
Darktan	Yes, sir.
Hamnpork	Need … to … sleep. Nourishing … tells me … you saw the … tunnel … of the … Big Rat.

*Darktan glares at **Nourishing**, who looks embarrassed.*

Darktan	I saw … something, yes.
Hamnpork	Then I shall dream my way there and … never wake up. This isn't … the way a … an old rat should die. Not … like this. Not … in the light.

*Darktan nods urgently at **Sardines**, who extinguishes the candle.*

You need to know this …

*Darktan leans over as **Hamnpork** whispers to him. **Hamnpork** dies. **Darktan** stands up again. One of the rats lights the candle again.*

Rat	Do we have to eat him now?
Darktan	He's … gone. Bury him. And mark the place so we know he's there.

Rat	Er … when you say 'mark the place', do you mean like we mark other places where we bury things?
Other rat	He means by widdling on it.
Darktan	Yes. He'd like that. It's very … ratty. But draw a sign in the dirt above him to show he was a rat from a long line of rats and he thought about rats.
Sardines	Good one, boss.
Rat	Will he come back, like Darktan did?
Darktan	Listen, I didn't …
Sardines	A word in your ear, guv?

Sardines pulls Darktan to one side.

	You know, I use to hang around the theatre an' that. And you pick up stuff in the theatre. What I'm saying is, you're the leader, right? So you got to act like you know what you're doing, OK?
Darktan	I only know what I'm doing when I'm dismantling traps.
Sardines	All right, think of the future as a great big trap. With no cheese.
Darktan	That's not a lot of help!
Sardines	And let them think what they like about you and … that scar you've got. That's my advice, guv.
Darktan	But I didn't die, Sardines!
Sardines	Are you sure? *Something* happened, didn't it? Seems to me, boss, that anyone who could stare down the Bone Rat … well, no one is going to want to mess with *him*, right? People will follow a rat like that.
Darktan	I'll have to watch you, Sardines. You think like Maurice.
Sardines	Don't worry about me, boss. I wouldn't be any good at leadering.
Darktan	Where *is* Dangerous Beans?
Sardines	Haven't seen him, boss.

Darktan	We need him. He's got the map in his head. The map of who we are and where we're going. I need to talk to him. When I was in that … place, I saw the shape of an idea. There's been a war between humans and rats for ever. It's got to end. And here, now, with these rats … I can see it happen. I can see the shape of the idea, but I can't think of the *words*, understand? I need Dangerous Beans, because he knows the map for thinking. We've got to think our way out of this. Running around and squeaking won't work any more. We need him. I need him.
Sardines	I'll get some squads together, boss, if you show me where to start looking.
Darktan	In the drains not far from the cages. Maurice was with him.
Sardines	Guv? What was it Hamnpork whispered to you just before he died? Special leader wisdom, was it?
Darktan	Good advice. Good advice.

He turns to the other rats.

OK. Now, we don't know where we're going. There's something new down here. Something tough. Something strong. And it's *you*. Rats who can think. Rats who don't turn and run. Nothing can stop rats like you, right?

Murmur of agreement.

You remember the Dark Wood from the book? Well, we're in the Dark Wood now. And there's something else down here. Something terrible, and it hides behind your fear. Well, we're going to find it and drag it out and we're gonna make it wish we'd never been *born*!

And if we die – well, death ain't so bad. Cos me and the Bone Rat … we've got a little understanding. He waits for those who break and run. But if you stare straight into his eyes, he'll give you a nod, and pass on.

And afterwards, people will say 'they went there and they did it'.

Ready to die for the clan, Sardines?

Sardines	No, boss – ready to kill!
	The rats cheer.
Darktan	Good. Let's go. We love the Dark Wood! It belongs to us!
	*The rats cheer and run off after **Darktan**. Black out.*

SCENE 6

	*The lair of the **Rat King**. **Peaches** and **Dangerous Beans** enter.*
Peaches	I dropped 'Mr Bunnsy'.
Dangerous Beans	Good. It was just a lie. Lies drag us down.
Peaches	And … I've lost the rules, too.
Dangerous Beans	So? No one bothered with them, either.
Peaches	That's not true! People tried to. Mostly. And they were sorry when they didn't.
Dangerous Beans	They were just another story about rats who thought they weren't rats.
Peaches	Why are you talking like this? This isn't like you!
Dangerous Beans	It was all so clear to me …
Peaches	Lie down. You're tired. I've got a few matches left. You always feel better when you see a light …
	She goes to light a match.
Rat King	*[Off]* And so – in your despair, you come, at last, to me!
Dangerous Beans	Who are you?
Rat King	*[Off]* I am the Big Rat That Lives Underground. Two more matches, little rat – and then, one way or another, you belong to me!
	Maurice enters, but almost immediately freezes to the spot.
Peaches	Maurice!
Rat King	*[Off]* The cat will not move. Or I will command his lungs to stop. See, little rat? Even a cat obeys me.
Dangerous Beans	Yes … command, obey … I see you have a power.
Rat King	*[Off]* Clever rat. I have heard you talk to the others. You understand the truth. You know about the darkness in front of

us and the darkness behind our eyes. You know that we cooperate or die.

Maurice Cooperate? Like these other rats? They smell strong and stupid.

Rat King *[Off]* But the strong survive. As for their minds – I can think for everyone.

Dangerous Beans Alas, I am not strong.

Rat King *[Off]* You have an interesting mind. You have worked out that there is a race in this world which steals and kills and spreads disease and despoils what it cannot use.

Dangerous Beans That's easy. It's called humanity.

Rat King *[Off]* Well done. See my fine rats? In a few hours the silly rat piper will play his silly rat pipe and yes, my rats will scamper after him out of town. Do you know how a piper kills rats?

Dangerous Beans No.

Rat King *[Off]* He leads them to the river and drowns them.

Dangerous Beans But rats are good swimmers.

Rat King *[Off]* Exactly! Never trust a rat-catcher! They will leave themselves work for tomorrow. Humans like to believe stories – they would prefer to believe stories than to believe the truth! We will pay them back a thousandfold for every trap! Humans have tortured and poisoned and killed and now there will be REVENGE!

Dangerous Beans From you. I begin to understand. I want to see who I am talking to.

Rat King *[Off]* You are blind, little rat. Through your pink eyes I see only mist.

Dangerous Beans I see more than you think. If you are, as they say, the Big Rat … then show yourself to me. Smelling is believing.

*The **Rat King** comes into the light.*

Rat King	Then tell me the truth, rat. Do you see me? Yes, you see me, in your mist. Men made me for sport! Tie the rats' tails together and watch them struggle! But I did not struggle – together we are strong! My time is near. The stupid men let rats fight and the strong survive, and then *they* fight, and the strongest of the strong survive … and soon the cages will open and men shall know the meaning of the word 'plague'. We want the same things. We have plans. Join us. Together we will be STRONG!
Dangerous Beans	Your offer is … interesting.
Rat King	Indeed!
Dangerous Beans	But what of those who *aren't* strong, please?
Rat King	The weak are food. That's how it has always been.
Peaches	Don't listen to it! It's affecting your mind!
Dangerous Beans	No, my mind is working perfectly, thank you. Yes, the proposition is beguiling. And we would rule the rat world together, would we?
Rat King	We would … cooperate.
Maurice	Yeah, *you* cooperate, *they* rule. Surely you can't fall for this!
Dangerous Beans	Together we could give humans a war they won't believe. Of course, millions of rats would die …
Rat King	They die anyway!
Dangerous Beans	Mmm. Yes. That is true. But it would not work.
Rat King	Would not work?
Dangerous Beans	Because, you see, you just think *for* many rats. But you don't think *of* them. Nor are you the Big Rat. Every word you utter is a lie. If there is a Big Rat, it would be made of the best that we could be, not the worst that we are. No, I will not join you, liar in the dark. I prefer our way. We are silly and weak, sometimes. But together *we* are strong. You have plans for rats? Well, I have dreams for them.

Rat King	So – you think you are a good rat? You think a good rat is a rat in a waistcoat? Oh yes, I know about your stupid book! Traitor! Traitor to rats! Will you feel my … PAIN!

*Effect. The rats writhe in agony. **Maurice** is affected really badly.*

Maurice	No! What's happening to me?
Rat King	I will strip your mind of its 'education' and 'knowledge', cat! I will turn you back into just a normal cat!
Maurice	No-o-o!
Rat King	You defy me? When I am everything that is truly RAT? I am filth and darkness! I am the noise under the floor, the rustling in the walls! I am the sum of all you deny! I am your true self! Will you OBEY ME?
Dangerous Beans	Never. You are nothing but shadows.
Rat King	Feel my PAIN!

*Effect. The rats writhe again. **Maurice**, again, is badly affected.*

Peaches	Maurice! Don't give in! Remember what you are! You are not just a cat!
Dangerous Beans	Yes, I feel the pain. I am a rat, but I am not vermin.
Rat King	VERMIN?
Dangerous Beans	Once we were just another squeaking thing in the forest. And then humans built barns and pantries full of food. Of course, we took what we could. And so they called us vermin, and they have trapped us and poisoned us and somehow, out of that wretchedness, *you* have come. You are just another bad thing humans made. You offer rats nothing but more pain. You just have a power to enter people's minds when they are tired or weak or stupid or upset. And you are in mine now.
Rat King	Yes. Oh yes.
Dangerous Beans	And still I stand here. I know you. You have the smell of the Bone Rat about you. Even though my body is shaking, I can keep a place free from you. I can control the shadows inside. I am more

84

	than just a rat. If I am *not* more than a rat, I am nothing at all.
Rat King	THEN BE NOTHING!
	*An excrutiating sound. Many of the rats collapse. FIGHT SCENE. In slow motion we see **Maurice** spring at the **Rat King**, going straight for its tail knot. He bites it through and the **Rat King** separates into individual panicking rats, who all run around aimlessly. **Maurice** fights with many rats, killing several in his raw anger, but also being injured badly himself. Suddenly, the only rat left standing is **Dangerous Beans**. **Maurice** sees him.*
Peaches	Maurice! Maurice! Try to remember!
	***Maurice** pounces on **Dangerous Beans** as the lights black out.*
Dangerous Beans	Maurice!
	***Peaches** walks to the lectern.*
Peaches	*[Reading]* And there he found Mr Bunnsy, tangled in the brambles and his blue coat all torn.
	***Peaches** walks to her place in the next scene.*

● ●

SCENE 7

	*The **Rat King's** lair. There are dead rats lying around. **Peaches** is to one side, muttering to herself. **Keith**, **Malicia**, **Darktan**, **Sardines**, and **Nourishing** enter.*
Darktan	What's happened here?
Sardines	Looks like a war, guv. Isn't that Peaches?
	They cross to her.
Darktan	Are you all right, Peaches? What's happened to Dangerous Beans?
	***Peaches** points to another part of the stage and lights come up to reveal **Maurice** standing over **Dangerous Beans'** body. **Maurice** sways slightly, on the point of collapse.*
Sardines	Maurice?

Darktan	What's he done to Dangerous Beans?
	*Maurice collapses by **Dangerous Beans**' body. Lights out on the other rats. Blue light up on **Maurice** and **Dangerous Beans** as **Death** enters.*
Death	Ah, Maurice. I haven't seen you much lately.
	Maurice stands up.
Maurice	No, sir. Been very careful, sir. Looking both ways when I cross the street and everything, sir.
Death	And how many do you have left now?
Maurice	Six, sir. Six. Six left out of nine. Very definitely six lives, sir.
Death	But you were run over by a cart only last month, weren't you?
Maurice	That sir? Barely grazed me, sir. Got away with hardly a scratch, sir.
Death	Exactly.
Maurice	Oh.
Death	That makes five lives, Maurice. Up until today's adventure.
Maurice	Fair enough, fair enough. So, um, let's say I'm left with three, right?
Death	Three? I was only going to take one. You can't lose more than one life at a time, even if you're a cat. That leaves you four, Maurice.
Maurice	[Indicating **Dangerous Beans**' body] And I say, take *two*, sir. Two, and call it quits?
Death	Are you sure? After all, he is a rat.

Maurice	Yes, sir. That's where it gets complicated, sir. Don't know why, sir. Everything's been a bit odd, lately.
Death	That is very un-cat-like of you, Maurice. I'm amazed.
Maurice	I'm pretty shocked, too, sir. I just hope no one finds out, sir.
Death	Very well. I came for two, and two I shall take. The balance is preserved.
Maurice	Sir? I suppose there isn't a Big *Cat* in the sky, is there?
Death	I'm surprised at you, Maurice. Of course there are no cat gods. That would be too much like … work.
Maurice	*[Nodding at this]* And … I won't remember this, will I? It'd be just too embarrassing.
Death	*[Departing]* Of course not, Maurice …
	*As **Death** leaves, the normal lights come up, and **Darktan** and the others cross to **Maurice** and **Dangerous Beans**. **Dangerous Beans** is moving a little and the rats go to him. **Keith's** speech follows seamlessly on from **Death's** last line.*
Keith	Maurice? We thought you were dead! Are you all right?
Maurice	Is the little rat okay?
Keith	He's not well, but he's getting better. We were going to release all the caged rats, but …
Malicia	Then we didn't. We came to our senses – it must have been when you killed the Rat King.
Maurice	All's well that ends … ow! It hurts when I move.
Keith	You're covered in rat bites, that's why.
Maurice	Well, adventure over, time for tea and buns, just like the girl says.
Keith	No, there's still the piper. I have a plan.
Maurice	*You* have a plan? *You* made it up?
Keith	Me and Darktan and Malicia.

ACT 2   SCENE 7

Malicia	We're going to keep the ordinary rats caged up so no rats will come out to follow the piper. He'll be so embarrassed, he'll leave.
Maurice	That's *it*? That's your plan? You don't know anything about people, do you?
Malicia	What? I'm a person!
Maurice	So? *Cats* know about people. We have to. No one else can open cupboards. Look, even the Rat King would've had a better plan than that. A good plan isn't one where someone wins, it's where no one thinks they've *lost*. Understand? Now, this is what we'll do, and we're going to need a lot of cotton wool …
Malicia	*[Reaching for her bag]* As a matter of fact …
Maurice	You're going to say that you've got a lot of cotton wool, aren't you?
Malicia	Yes!
Maurice	It was silly of me to worry, wasn't it?
	Black out.

• •

SCENE 8

*The town square. Some villagers are onstage, as is the **Mayor**. **Sergeant Doppelpunkt** runs on.*

Doppelpunkt	Mr Mayor, Mr Mayor! The rat piper is here, sir!
Mayor	Quick! Help me on with my robe and hat! Over in Klotz, the mayor kept the rat piper waiting and he turned him into a *badger!*
	*The **Rat Piper** saunters on, with his **Agent**. He surveys the town square.*
Rat Piper	So – this is what you call a town square, is it?
Doppelpunkt	Er … yes, sir!

Rat Piper	*[To the Mayor]* And you are … ?
Mayor	I am the mayor of this town and –
Rat Piper	My agent will deal with you.
	He walks off and sits on a bench to one side.
Mayor	What? How dare –
Doppelpunkt	Remember the badger, sir.
Mayor	Oh. Yes. *[Turning to the Agent]* I believe the fee for ridding the town of rats will be three hundred dollars?
Agent	Then I expect you'd believe *anything*. Let's see, there's call-out fee, plus pipe tax, wear and tear on cart, travelling costs at a dollar a mile, extra charge for a medium-sized town … tell you what, let's say one thousand dollars, OK?
Mayor	A thousand dollars! We haven't *got* one thousand dollars! That's outrag –
Doppelpunkt	Badger, sir!
Agent	You can't pay?
Mayor	We don't have that kind of money!
Agent	Difficult. Because, let's see … *[Checking his notebook]* You already owe us four hundred and sixty-seven dollars and nineteen pence for call-out, travel, and miscellaneous sundries.
Mayor	What? He hasn't even blown one note!
	Keith, Malicia, *and* ***Maurice*** *enter silently and join the crowd.*
Agent	Ah, but he's *ready* to. We've come all this way. He's got to lead *something* out of town. Otherwise word will get round and no-one'll show him any respect, and if you haven't got respect, what have you got? If a piper don't have respect, he's –
Keith	*[Stepping forward]* Rubbish. I think he's rubbish.
	The piper stands and joins the group.
Rat Piper	Yeah?

Keith	I don't think he can pipe up even one rat. He's just a fraud and a bully. I bet I can pipe up more rats than him.
Rat Piper	You a rat piper, kid?
Keith	Yes. And don't call me kid, old man.
Rat Piper	*[Grinning]* I *knew* I was going to like this place. And you can make a rat dance, can you kid?
Keith	More than you can, piper.
Rat Piper	Sounds like a challenge to me. This isn't the first time some kid has tried this. I'm walking down the street and some kid shouts, 'Go for your piccolo, mister', and I turn round and it's always a kid like you with a stupid-looking face. If you'd just care to apologise you might just walk away from here with the same number of legs you started with –
Malicia	You're *frightened!*
Rat Piper	Yeah?
Malicia	Yeah, because everyone knows what happens at a time like this. Let me ask this stupid-looking kid, whom I've never seen before: are you an orphan?
Keith	Yes.
Malicia	Do you know nothing about your background?
Keith	No.
Malicia	Aha! That proves it! We *all* know what happens when a mysterious orphan turns up and challenges someone big and powerful, don't we? He can't help but win!
Maurice	*[From the back of the crowd]* Give the stupid-looking kid a chance! At least he'll be cheaper!
	He moves round the crowd a bit.
	Yes, that's right!
	Moving again.
	I agree with the other two!

Rat Piper	Fine. And when I win, what will I get?
Mayor	Is a daughter's hand in marriage usual in these circumstances?
Malicia	Father!
Rat Piper	No, I'll just take my payment. One way or another.
Mayor	But I said we can't afford it!
Rat Piper	And I said one way or another. And you, kid?
Keith	Your rat pipe.
Rat Piper	No. It's magic, kid.
Keith	Then why are you scared to bet it?
Rat Piper	Scared? OK, the rat pipe.
Keith	And the town must let me solve its rat problem.
Mayor	And how much will *you* charge?
Maurice	*[From the back of the crowd]* Thirty gold pieces! Thirty gold pieces! Go on, say it!
Keith	It won't cost you a thing.
Maurice	*[From the crowd]* Idiot!
Mayor	Nothing at all? The hand-in-marriage thing is still on offer, you know …
Malicia	Father!
Keith	No, that only happens in stories. I shall also bring back a lot of the food the rats stole.
Mayor	But they *ate* it! What're you going to do? Stick your fingers down their throats?
Keith	But first, I need to borrow a pipe. Mine got broken.
Doppelpunkt	I have a trombone from when I was in the army.
	Keith nods. Doppelpunkt exits.
Rat Piper	A trombone? For charming rats? Good with a trombone, are you?

Keith	I don't know. I've never played one.
	*Doppelpunkt re-enters with the trombone. **Keith** blows it and gets a note from it.*
	Seems to work. I expect I can learn as I go along. Do you want to go first?
Rat Piper	No, no – after *you!*
	***Keith** starts to play. **Sardines** appears, with hat and cane, and performs a short dance routine. **Keith** stops playing and **Sardines** exits.*
	Did that one have a *hat* on?
Keith	Didn't notice. Your turn.
	The piper puts his pipe to his lips and plays. We hear nothing.
	Just one rat. Any rat you like. No rush.
	The piper plays again.
Mayor	I can't hear anything.
Rat Piper	*[Pausing briefly]* Humans can't.
	He plays again.
Keith	Perhaps it's broken.
	The crowd start to laugh.
Rat Piper	You've done something!
Malicia	Oh yes? What could he have done? Told the rats to stay underground with their ears blocked with cotton wool?
	More laughter from the crowd. Suddenly, a rat emerges. It staggers robotically across the stage before falling at the rat piper's feet. Now we see it has a clockwork key in its back, bearing the inscription, 'Mr Clicky'. The crowd laugh hysterically. We hear 'it's only a clockwork rat' from someone.
Rat Piper	OK, kid. Shall you and I have a little talk? Over here?

Keith	*[As they move away from the crowd]* Provided people can still see us.
Rat Piper	You don't trust me, kid?
Keith	Of course not.
Rat Piper	*[Grinning]* Good. Well done.
	*He hands **Keith** his rat pipe.*
	Here, take it. It's a good one. I've got plenty of others. It's *all* trickery, kid. See the slider on the side? Move it down and the pipe plays a special note only rats can hear. Sends 'em nuts. They come rushing out and you drive 'em into the river. Just like a sheepdog.
Keith	That's all there is to it? They say you turn people into badgers and lead children into magic caves and –
Rat Piper	*[Leaning in, conspiratorially]* It always pays to advertise, kid. Sometimes these small towns can be pretty slow when it comes to parting with the cash. And the thing about the turning people into badgers is, it never happens *round here.* These small-town people don't travel much and they'll believe just about anything could happen fifty miles away. Once the story gets round, it does your work for you. Half the things people say I've done even I didn't make up!
Keith	Have you ever met someone called Maurice?
Rat Piper	Maurice? Maurice? Don't think so.
Keith	Amazing. And now, piper, you're going to lead the rats out of the town. It's going to be the most impressive job you've ever done.
Rat Piper	What? But *you* won, kid!
Keith	You'll lead the rats out because that's how it should go. Why do you charge such a lot?
Rat Piper	Because I give 'em a *show.* You've got to give 'em magic, kid.
Keith	We'll do it together, and the rats will follow us, *really* follow us to the river. Don't bother about your trick note, because this

	will be even better And you'll get your money – three hundred dollars? – but you'll settle for half, because I'm helping you.
Rat Piper	What are you playing at, kid? I told you, you won.
Keith	Everyone wins. Trust me. They called you in. They should pay the piper. *[Smiling]* I don't want people to think pipers shouldn't get paid, do I?
Rat Piper	And I thought you were just a stupid-looking kid. What kind of *deal* have you got with the rats?
Keith	You wouldn't believe it, piper. You wouldn't believe it.

*Black out. **Maurice** walks forward into a spot.*

Maurice	And so, the order was given and the rats unblocked their ears and the drains – now drawn by the music, they followed the pipers. How the crowd yelled when the rats erupted from every hole and drain. How they cheered when both pipers danced out of the town, with the rats racing along behind them. How they whistled when the rats plunged off the bridge into the river. And the big piper danced off over the hills and never, ever came back.

*Light out on **Maurice**. **Peaches** walks to the lectern.*

Peaches	*[Reading]* 'Well done, Ratty Rupert' cried the animals of Furry Bottom.

*Peaches walks to her place in the next scene. The lights come back up on the town square. The villagers, **Malicia**, **Maurice**, and **Doppelpunkt** are onstage. The **Mayor** is shaking **Keith** by the hand. **Darktan**, **Peaches**, **Dangerous Beans**, **Sardines**, **Nourishing**, and the other rats enter.*

Mayor	Here, piper … you missed some!
Darktan	No. We're not the rats who follow pipers. We're the rats you have to *deal with*.
Malicia	Father, it would be a good idea to listen to this rat.
Mayor	But it's a rat!

Malicia	But he knows how to get your money back and a lot of the food and where to find some of the people who've been stealing it.
Mayor	We should talk to rats?
Malicia	Yes, father.
Mayor	But they're *rats!*
Maurice	'Scuse me, 'scuse me.
Mayor	Did that cat just *speak?*
Maurice	Which one?
Mayor	You! Did you just talk?
Maurice	Would you feel better if I said no?
Keith	Mr Mayor, don't you think it's time I sorted out your rat problem once and for all? All you have to do is talk to them. You can yell or shout and call out the dogs and people can flail at the rats with brooms and, yes, they'll run away. But they won't run far. And they'll come back. And they know how to use fire, sir. They know *all* about poison. So … listen to this rat.
Mayor	Is it … *threatening* us?
Darktan	No, Mr Mayor. I'm offering you … *[glancing at **Maurice**, who nods]* … a wonderful opportunity.
Mayor	You really can talk? You can think?
Darktan	Here's what I suggest. You pretend that rats can think, and I'll promise to pretend that humans can think, too.
	Black out.

• •

SCENE 9

*The **Mayor**'s office. The **Mayor**, a couple of **Councillors**, **Keith**, **Malicia**, **Darktan**, **Peaches**, and **Sardines** are sitting around a meeting table. **Sergeant Doppelpunkt** enters, carrying a large chest.*

Mayor	Where are the rat-catchers?

Doppelpunkt	In deep … trouble, sir. They said they'd confess to everything in exchange for a drink of water and some fresh trousers. And there's this, sir. Acting on information received from a rat, sir, we took a look under the floorboards in their shed. There must be more'n two hundred dollars in it.

He puts the chest onto the table, salutes, and exits.

Mayor	Now, where were we?
Maurice	I was going to tell you a story. But first, I'm going to tell you that my clients, the rats, will leave this town if you want them to and they won't come back. Ever.
Darktan	Will we?
Mayor	Will they?
Maurice	Yes. And now, I'm going to tell you a story about the lucky town. I don't know its name yet. Let's suppose my clients leave here and move down river, shall we? Somewhere there'll be a town that'll say, why, we *can* do a deal with the rats. And that will be a very lucky town because then there will be *rules*, see?
Mayor	Not exactly, no.
Maurice	Well, in this lucky town, right, a lady making, as it might be, a tray of cakes, well all she'll need to do is to shout down the nearest rat hole and say, 'Good morning, rats, there's one cake for you, I'll be much obliged if you didn't touch the rest of them', and the rats will say, 'Right you are, missus, no problem at all'. And then –
Mayor	Are you saying we should *bribe* the rats?
Maurice	Cheaper than pipers. Cheaper than rat-catchers. Anyway, it'll be wages. Wages for what, I hear you cry?
Mayor	Did I cry that?
Maurice	You were going to. And I was going to say it'd be wages for … vermin control.
Mayor	What? But rats *are* ver –

Darktan	Don't say it!
Maurice	*[Smoothly]* Vermin like cockroaches. You have lots of them.
Mayor	Can *they* talk?
Maurice	No. Nor can the mice, and nor can normal – nor can *other* rats. Well, vermin will be a thing of the past in that lucky town, because its new rats will be like a police force. The Clan will *guard* your larders – sorry, I mean, the larders in that town. No rat-catchers required. But that's only the start. The woodcarvers will get richer, too.
Mayor	Why?
Maurice	Tiny little paws, very good with little springs and things. And then there's the whole tourism aspect. You know that clock they have in the town square of Byonk? Little figures come out every quarter of an hour and clang bells? Big attraction. You can get postcards. People come a long way just to stand there waiting for it.
Mayor	So, what you're saying is, if we – that is, if the lucky town had a special big clock, and rats, people might come to see it?
Maurice	And stand around waiting for up to quarter of an hour – a perfect time to buy tooth-crafted models of the clock, mugs with rats on, hand-gnawed wooden souvenir plates. And I expect the town would want to employ its very own rat piper – for ceremonial purposes. 'Have Your Picture Drawn with the Official Rat Piper and his Rats', sort of thing.
Sardines	Any chance of a small theatre?
Darktan	Sardines!
Sardines	Well, guv, I just thought if everyone was getting in on the act!
Maurice	*[To the Mayor]* Excuse me, I just need to consult with my clients. Of course, I'm talking about the *lucky* town. Which won't be this one, of course, because when my clients move out some other rats will move in. And *they* won't talk, and *they* won't have rules, and they'll widdle in the cream and you'll

have to find some new rat-catchers and you won't have as much money because everyone will be going to the other town. Just a thought.

He draws the rats to one side.

Darktan	Is this what we fought for? To be *pets?*
Dangerous Beans	Maurice, this isn't right.
Maurice	Listen. Ten minutes ago these people thought you were pests. Now they think you're … useful. Think what I can achieve in another half hour!
Darktan	You want us to *work* for them? We've *won* our place here!
Maurice	You'll be working for *yourself*. These people aren't philosophers. They don't understand about life in the tunnels. You've got to approach them in the right way. You'll keep other rats away and you won't widdle in the cream any more *anyway*, so you might as well get paid for it!
Sardines	He's right boss – you gotta give 'em a show.
Darktan	They'll laugh at us!
Sardines	Better laugh than scream, boss. It's a start.
Dangerous Beans	I'd hoped there'd be an island somewhere. A place where rats could really be rats.
Darktan	And we've seen where *that* leads. If there's a wonderful island somewhere, it's here.

Keith and Malicia cross to them.

Malicia	I think my father's coming round to the idea. What about you?
Maurice	Discussions are continuing.
Malicia	[*To Peaches*] I … er, I'm sorry. Maurice told me where to look and I found this in the tunnel.

She produces the now battered, water-damaged copy of 'Mr Bunnsy'.

Peaches	*[To **Dangerous Beans**]* It's 'Mr Bunn' –
Dangerous Beans	I know. I can smell it.
Peaches	It's a lie.
Sardines	Maybe it's just a pretty story.
Dangerous Beans	Yes. Yes. Perhaps it's a map.
Mayor	*[Crossing over to them and speaking to Darktan]* Excuse me. Could I have a word?

*He and **Darktan** cross away from the others, who move back up to the table, talking (silently). **Keith** and **Malicia** cross to the opposite side of the stage.*

I'm going to get this wrong. I thought we should have a little … talk.

Pause.

Do you have much paperwork in your job?

Darktan	Peaches writes things down.
Mayor	That's the little female rat that coughs before she speaks, isn't it?
Darktan	That's right.
Mayor	You, er, settling in well?
Darktan	*[Coldly]* I spent part of last night fighting a dog in a rat pit, and then I think I was stuck in a rat trap for a while. And then there was a bit of a war. Apart from that, I can't complain.

*He looks at the **Mayor**, who looks tired and worn down.*

Look, I think it might work, if that's what you want to ask me.

Mayor	You do?

He looks across at the table, where the rats and the humans are in (silent) heated discussion.

There's a lot of arguing.

Darktan	That's why I think it'll work. Men and rats arguing. You're not poisoning our cheese, and we're not widdling in your jam. It's not going to be easy, but it's a start.
Mayor	But there's something I have to know.
Darktan	Yes?
Mayor	You *could* have poisoned our wells, you *could* have set fire to our houses. My daughter tells me you are very advanced. You don't owe us anything. Why didn't you?
Darktan	I asked myself that, too. And I told myself: what good would it do? What would we have done afterwards? Gone to another town? Gone through all this again? Would killing you have made anything *better* for us? Sooner or later we'd have to talk to humans. It might as well be you. I want to ask *you* a question. You've been the leader for ... how long?
Mayor	Ten years.
Darktan	Isn't it hard?
Mayor	Oh yes. Yes. Everyone argues with me all the time. It's not an easy job.
Darktan	It's ridiculous to have to keep shouting all the time just to get things done.
Mayor	That's right.
Darktan	And everyone expects you to decide things.
Mayor	True.
Darktan	The last leader gave me some advice just before he died. Know what it was? 'Don't eat the green wobbly bit.'
Mayor	Good advice?
Darktan	In his world, yes. But all *he* had to do was be big and tough and fight all the other rats who wanted to be leader.
Mayor	It's a bit like that with the town council.
Darktan	What? You bite them on the neck?

Mayor	Not yet. But it's a tempting thought, though.
Darktan	It's just all a lot more complicated than I ever thought it would be! To be a leader you have to learn to shout! But after you've learned to shout you have to learn not to.
Mayor	Right again. That's how it works. I have to make sure the town works. And every year it turns out I haven't upset enough people for them to choose anyone else as mayor, so I have to do it all again. It's a lot more complicated than I ever thought it would be!
Darktan	What? For you, too? But you're a human!
Mayor	Hah! You think that makes it easier? I thought rats were wild and free!
Darktan	Hah!
Mayor	Er … you could have a little desk in my office, if you like?
Darktan	No thanks. Little desks are a bit too … Mr Bunnsy.
Mayor	I suppose so. I did like those books when I was a boy, though. I knew it was all nonsense, of course, but it was nice to think that –
Darktan	Yeah, yeah. But the rabbit was stupid. Whoever heard of a rabbit talking?
Mayor	Oh yes. I never liked the rabbit.
Darktan	No one likes the rabbit.
Mayor	It's like I always tell my daughter. Stories are just stories. Life is complicated enough as it is. We have to plan for the real world. There's no room for the fantastic.
Darktan	Exactly.
	*They walk back up to the rest of the meeting, and all now exit except for **Keith** and **Malicia**. Light now comes up on **Keith** and **Malicia**.*
Malicia	It was odd about Maurice, wasn't it, when my father said to him that there would be plenty of kind old ladies who'd be happy to give him a home?

Keith	You mean when he said it wouldn't be any fun, getting it that way?
Malicia	Yes. Do you know what he meant?
Keith	Sort of. He meant he's *Maurice*. He's no one's pet.
	Pause.
Malicia	And, er … you're staying, yes?
Keith	Resident Rat Piper. I get an official suit, a hat with a feather, and a pipe allowance.
Malicia	That will be … quite satisfactory. Er …
Keith	Yes?
Malicia	When I told you I had two sisters … that wasn't entirely true. Er … it wasn't a lie, of course, but it was just, enhanced a bit.
Keith	Yes.
Malicia	I mean, it would be more *literally* true to say that I have, in fact, no sisters at all.
Keith	Ah.
Malicia	But I have millions of friends, of course.
Keith	That's amazing. Most people just have a few dozen.
Malicia	Millions.
	Pause.
	Obviously, there is always room for another one.
Keith	Good.
Malicia	And … er, of course, there's still the slap-up tea with cream buns and a medal. Um, it wouldn't be properly over, otherwise. Would you, er, join me?
Keith	Yes. Yes. I think I'll stay.
	*Black out. They exit. Follow spot on **Maurice**.*

| Maurice | So. That's that. It's not perfect, but it works. The thing about stories is that you have to pick the ones that will last. Me? I'm off to a new town, me. New challenges. |

A boy walks across the stage. He is carrying a stick over his shoulder, on one end of which is a knotted handkerchief of the sort used by people in story circumstances to carry all their worldly goods. Maurice watches him cross the stage. As soon as he's left, Maurice turns back to the audience.

If you know their dreams, you can handle people. *[calling after the boy]*

Hey, stupid-looking kid! Wanna be Lord Mayor?

He exits after the boy as the lights black out.

THE END

Activities

KEY STAGE 3 FRAMEWORK OBJECTIVES	RELEVANT ACTIVITIES CHAPTER(S)
Sentence Level	
12 Sequencing paragraphs	Animal Baiting
13 Stylistic conventions (Instructions)	Animal Baiting, Traditional Tales and Rules
17 Standard English	Traditional Tales and Rules
Reading	
1 Locate information	Characters, Following the Leader, Traditional Tales and Rules
2 Extract information	Characters, Following the Leader, Traditional Tales and Rules
4 Note-making	Characters, Traditional Tales and Rules
7 Identify main ideas	Traditional Tales and Rules
12 Character, setting and mood	Characters
13 Non-fiction style	Animal Baiting
14 Language choices	Characters, Animal Baiting
20 Literary heritage	Traditional Tales and Rules
Writing	
1 Drafting process	Animal Baiting, On the Stage
2 Planning formats	Following the Leader, Traditional Tales and Rules
3 Exploratory writing	Traditional Tales and Rules
12 Develop logic	On the Stage
14 Evocative description	On the Stage
15 Express a view	Animal Baiting
16 Validate an argument	Animal Baiting
18 Present findings	On the Stage
Speaking and Listening	
1 Clarify through talk	Following the Leader, The Battle
3 Shape a presentation	Animal Baiting
4 Answers, instructions, explanations	Following the Leader
5 Put a point of view	Following the Leader
6 Recall main points	Following the Leader, Animal Baiting
7 Pertinent questions	Following the Leader
8 Presentational techniques	Following the Leader, Animal Baiting
9 Oral text types	Animal Baiting
10 Report main points	Traditional Tales and Rules
11 Range of roles	Characters, Following the Leader
12 Exploratory talk	Characters, Traditional Tales and Rules
13 Collaboration	Characters, Following the Leader, Traditional Tales and Rules
14 Modify views	Characters, Following the Leader
15 Explore in role	Characters, Following the Leader, Animal Baiting, Drama Techniques
16 Collaborate on scripts	Following the Leader, The Battle, Animal Baiting, Drama Techniques

17	Extend spoken repertoire	Following the Leader, The Battle, Animal Baiting, Drama Techniques
18	Exploratory drama	The Battle, Drama Techniques
19	Evaluate presentations	Following the Leader, The Battle

• •

YEAR 8

KEY STAGE 3 FRAMEWORK OBJECTIVES	RELEVANT ACTIVITIES CHAPTER(S)

Reading

2	Independent research	Animal Baiting
3	Notemaking formats	Characters, Following the Leader, Traditional Tales and Rules
4	Versatile reading	Characters
5	Trace developments	Following the Leader, Traditional Tales and Rules
10	Development of key ideas	Traditional Tales and Rules
14	Literary conventions	Traditional Tales and Rules

Writing

2	Anticipate reader reaction	Animal Baiting, On the Stage
3	Writing to reflect	Following the Leader
10	Effective information	Traditional Tales and Rules, On the Stage
11	Explain complex ideas	Traditional Tales and Rules
12	Formal description	Animal Baiting, On the Stage
13	Present a case persuasively	Animal Baiting
17	Integrate evidence	Animal Baiting

Speaking and Listening

4	Commentary	Animal Baiting
7	Listen for specific purpose	Animal Baiting
8	Hidden messages	Following the Leader
10	Hypothesis and speculation	Characters, Following the Leader, Traditional Tales and Rules, The Battle
11	Building on others	Characters, Following the Leader, Traditional Tales and Rules, The Battle
12	Varied roles in discussion	Following the Leader, Traditional Tales and Rules
13	Evaluate own drama skills	The Battle
14	Dramatic techniques	Following the Leader, Animal Baiting, The Battle, Drama Techniques
15	Work in role	Characters, Following the Leader, Drama Techniques
16	Collaborative presentation	Following the Leader, Animal Baiting, The Battle, Drama Techniques

Characters

CHARACTER PROFILES

1 As a class, draw up a list of the main characters in the play.

2 In smaller groups, select a character, and use the playscript to build up a profile of that character. Think about:
- what the character says and how he or she says it
- what the character does
- how the other characters react to your chosen character
- the appearance of the character, e.g. age, attitude, anything that they wear or carry, etc.

Record your ideas in note form, for example as a spider diagram. See page 110 for an example.

HOT-SEATING A CHARACTER

When the character profiles are complete, choose one person in your group to role-play your character in a hot-seating exercise.

As a group, draw up a list of questions to put to the character. Another member of the group needs to take on the role of a TV or radio reporter, interviewing the character about what happened at Bad Blintz.

During the interview, both the reporter and character from the play should remain in role.

NAMES

In the play, Maurice explains that one of the rats called himself Sardines 'because he saw the name on a can and he thought it sounded cool' (Act 1, Scene 4).

Think about the names of all the rodents and the characters they refer to. The author's choice of names is not purely random. Consider the associations of some names and how these reflect on the characters. For example, 'Darktan' suggests an outdoor, healthy, weather-beaten character, possibly wearing military camouflage. The name suits the character as Darktan is active, resilient, brave, and an intelligent problem-solver who shows leadership and has the skills of a military commander. Note that he also organizes the rodents into 'squads'.

Imagine other characters who might have appeared in the play. Discuss what sort of personalities they might have, and what might be appropriate names. Remember that they must be from labels on cans, food tins, and signs.

Character Profile: Malicia

What she says and how she says it

General: imaginative; forthright; loves to link things to drama/adventure/fiction; bossy; used to getting her own way; has flashes of insight (e.g. Act 1, Scene 14: 'If you don't turn your life into a story, you just become a part of someone else's story'. She is aware of the need to take decisions, give direction to your life).

Act 1, Scene 4: boastful; always thinks she's right; thinks she's victim, but she's actually well looked after; ruthless to animals; clever at making deductions; reads a lot.

Act 1, Scene 14: insensitive when she reveals the truth about 'Mr Bunnsy'.

What she does

General: resourceful (has a bag full of things she might need in emergency, e.g. grappling hook, mirrors, etc.); streetwise (can pick locks); brave (confronts the rat-catchers); sense of fun (gives the rat-catchers laxatives); kindly at the end (returns the 'Mr Bunnsy' to Peaches.

Act 1, Scene 14: doesn't always take the lead in crisis (here Keith decides on a plan).

Malicia

How other characters respond to her

General: Keith allows himself to be led along to an extent, but he and Maurice think she's a bit extreme (e.g. they see the stupidity of special knocks on barn door); she does have some leadership qualities (e.g. is full of ideas).

Act 1, Scene 10: in confrontation with Keith, Keith is more thoughtful; Keith accuses Malicia of talking all the time instead of thinking.

Act 1, Scene 11: rat-catcher says, 'you, Miss, are too lippy by half'.

Appearance/costume

General: carries a capacious bag that contains an amazing number of items in case of emergencies; is young and dramatic-looking; imaginative; certainly not boring.

Following the Leader

DIFFERENT TYPES OF LEADERSHIP

Leadership is an important theme in the play. Hamnpork is the old, respected leader, but he is aware that Darktan may pose a threat to his leadership. As the rats change the way they think, some of them also want to change the way they live.

Draw up a list of differences between Hamnpork and Darktan (the list has been started for you, see below). Think about how these differences make them different types of leaders.

Hamnpork	Darktan
Big, strong, tough	Agile, fit, dextrous
A physical fighter, not particularly clever	Uses his brains to fight, not just strength
Believes in tradition, e.g. eating dead rats	Consults other people, e.g. Dangerous Beans
Old	
Does not want to share his knowledge	
Likes the dark	

DEBATE

Imagine that Darktan openly challenges Hamnpork's leadership and that both 'leaders' have supporters among the rats.

Hold a class debate about which character should be the leader. One student should take on the role of Hamnpork, another the role of Darktan. Other students could take on the roles of some of the other rats. Divide the class in half to support each character.

Step 1

Make notes in preparation for the debate. Think about:

- the need for physical strength and/or technical skills in a leader
- the value of tradition
- age and youth
- communication skills
- progression and development of new skills, e.g. writing
- the value of consulting and appreciating others
- a vision of the future
- the value of rules.

Step 2

Hamnpork presents his case, i.e. the reasons why he thinks he would make a good leader.

Step 3

Darktan presents his case, i.e. the reasons why he thinks he would make a good leader.

Step 4

The debate is opened to the 'public' (i.e. the other members of the class), who put forward their views.

Step 5

The whole class votes. The speaker with the most votes is appointed leader.

• •

A PERSUASIVE SPEECH

Look at Darktan's speech to the rats before they go to find Dangerous Beans and confront the Rat King.

Darktan is aiming to give the rats courage, to keep them together and to give them a sense of purpose. It is a persuasive speech.

1   Can you spot the following techniques that are often used in persuasive speeches?
    - Repetition
    - Short sentences
    - The use of first person plural
    - Rhetorical questions
    - Appeal to the emotions
    - A vision of success and achievement

2   Think about how this speech could be delivered effectively, e.g. which words would you emphasize, where would you pause, where would your voice be soft, where would it be loud, what body language/gestures would you use, etc.

3   In pairs, practise delivering this speech, to give it maximum effect. When you have rehearsed it, stand at the front of the class and deliver it. The rest of the class may offer constructive criticism.

4   Using the persuasive techniques demonstrated in Darktan's speech, prepare a speech of your own to encourage your followers to help you with a task, particularly one that might involve some danger. Remember that the speech must be short, to the point, emotive, memorable, and energizing.

Animal Baiting

The rat-baiting scene in the play is pivotal to the plot. It proves that the 'educated rodents' can outwit their enemies, whatever their size and power.

Animal baiting was a popular sport for hundreds of years. Animals, such as bears or bulls, were restrained or trapped, and then dogs were set on them. In 1835, Parliament passed an act that made bear-baiting, bull-baiting, and cockfighting illegal. However, animal baiting still continues in parts of Britain and in some other countries.

CAMPAIGN POSTER

1 Research the issue of animal baiting, using ICT as well as books. Use the information you gather to draw up a campaign poster against the sport. Consider:
   - your target readership
   - the purpose of the poster, e.g. to raise money, raise awareness, recruit active campaigners, etc.
   - facts about the sport
   - emotive vocabulary
   - a short, powerful message
   - the value of visuals
   - a strong heading
   - contact details for further information.

2 Design and produce your poster on a computer.

NEWSPAPER REPORT

1 Re-read Act 2, Scene 1.

2 Rewrite the events as a newspaper report for either
   a) a tabloid, or
   b) a broadsheet.

Think carefully about:
- your target audience
- the importance of the headline
- quotations (invent these – they could be from one or two of the following: a rat-catcher, Darktan, Hamnpork, Sardines, one of the spectators)
- a picture
- a caption
- setting the scene
- reporting the events
- the aftermath (read Scene 3 for more information about this).

3 When you have produced a first draft, give it to a partner to comment on. Then check it through, making corrections and editing as appropriate, before you produce your final version.

● ●

SPORTS COMMENTARY

1 Re-read Act 2, Scene 1, noting how the two radio commentators present the events:
  1. They welcome the listeners, and build up excitement before the event.
  2. They describe the location and setting.
  3. They begin to track the events, giving plenty of detail.
  4. They give some opinions.
  5. They pass the narrative between them, each reinforcing what the other says.
  6. Background noises and voices are included.
  7. They get caught up in the excitement of the action.
  8. They pass comment on the events.
  9. They bid their audience goodnight.

2 Record part of a televised football match, or another sporting event, on video – something with plenty of action and excitement. Watch the video with a partner and

present a commentary on the action. Remember to introduce yourselves, set the scene, and to comment on the action as well as describing what happens.

3   If possible, record your commentary on audiotape, then play it to the rest of the class. Invite constructive criticism. Did the commentary give a clear sequence of what was happening? Was it visually descriptive? Did it relay the excitement of the action?

Traditional Tales and Rules

Two themes that are woven into this story are traditional tales and rules. These themes are linked: the traditional tales portray a safe, balanced world, where good always wins, while the rules are what the rats are drawing up as they try to live in a more civilized and fair society.

● ●

TRADITIONAL TALES

1   Throughout this story, there are many references to traditional tales. Brainstorm these and note them down in an appropriate form.

2   In small groups, or pairs, discuss what we associate with such tales, thinking of specific examples, such as:
●   a moral order, in which good prevails and evil is defeated
●   a shared heritage, through generations
●   warnings about danger
●   rewarding the good
●   promoting qualities such as truthfulness, patience, and hard work
●   punishment of qualities such as anger, jealousy, and greed
●   comfort and entertainment.

3   Why do you think the author includes these tales?
a)   Identify places where he uses them for comic effect.
b)   Identify places where he uses them to reflect on the main plot of the story.

4   How did you react to the story of 'Mr Bunnsy' when it was first introduced? Did your feelings change as the story unfolded? Track your changing attitude towards 'Mr Bunnsy' through the playscript. Draw up a simple

time-line, highlighting your feelings at specific points in the play (one has been started for you below).

Opening: Peaches first reads the opening; seems very childish, comic, rather absurd	**Scene 2**: a warning about the 'Dark Wood'; preparing for a typical 'moral' tale	**Scene 7**: indication that the 'Adventure' might be not just the normal physical kind, but more complicated, possibly in your mind 'when you were standing still'

5   Malicia declares that 'Mr Bunnsy' is just 'stupid stuff' (Act 1, Scene 14). But in the end, she realizes its value and returns the book to Peaches (Act 2, Scene 9). Why is the story valuable, even though it is not literally 'true'?

● ●

RULES

1   In Act 1, Scene 3, Peaches reads out the rules. Dangerous Beans wants these things written down, so that all the rodents agree on how to behave, and can live together peacefully and happily. Some of these rules are statements (i.e. they assert a fact) and some are instructions (i.e. they say what can or cannot be done). Identify which is which.

2   In small groups, imagine you are on a desert island. The group is alone, without adults. There has been some arguing and fighting, so you decide that you need to agree on a set of rules. Discuss and draw up a list of rules (some may be statements, others may be instructions). Consider:
   ● how you will share out the food and water
   ● how you will organize the work (e.g. building shelters)
   ● how everyone can have their say
   ● how the group will make decisions that affect everyone
   ● whether you will have a leader
   ● what is forbidden
   ● what are fair punishments if the rules are broken
   ● who can change the rules.

One person in the group should write down the rules in a formal style, but only once the wording is agreed with the whole group.

The Battle

In Act 2, Scene 7, Keith and Malicia explain how they were about to release the caged rats when they suddenly came to their senses. In the novel, a battle ensues, between the Clan and the Rat King's rats.

1   Read the following extract from the novel.

Keith blinked. He had his hand on the latch of one of the rat cages.

The rats were watching him. All standing the same way, all watching his fingers. Hundreds of rats. They looked … hungry.

'Did you hear something?' said Malicia.

Keith lowered his hand very carefully, and took a couple of steps back.

'Why are we letting these out?' he said. 'It was like I'd been … dreaming …'

'I don't know. You're the rat boy.'

'But we *agreed* to let them out.'

'I … it was … I had a feeling that —'

'Rat kings can talk to people, can't they?' said Keith. 'Has it been talking to us?'

'But this is real life,' said Malicia.

'I thought it was an adventure,' said Keith.

'Damn! I forgot,' said Malicia. 'What're they doing?'

It was almost as if the rats were melting. They were no longer upright, attentive statues. Something like panic was spreading through them again.

Then other rats poured out of the walls, running madly across the floor. They were much bigger than the caged ones. One of them bit Keith on the ankle, and he kicked it away.

'Try to stamp on them but don't lose your balance, whatever you do!' he said. 'These are *not* friendly!'

'Tread on them?' said Malicia. 'Yuk!'

'You mean you haven't got anything in your bag to fight rats? This is a rat-catchers' lair! You've got plenty of stuff for pirates and bandits and robbers!'

'Yes, but there's never been a book about having an adventure in a rat-catcher's cellar!' Malicia shouted. 'Ow! One's on my neck! One's on my neck! And there's another one!' She bent down frantically to shake the rats loose and reared up as one leapt at her face.

Keith grabbed her hand. '*Don't* fall over! They'll go mad if you do! Try to get to the door!'

'They're so fast!' Malicia panted. 'Now there's another one on my *hair—* '

'Hold still, stupid female!' said a voice in her ear. 'Hold quite still or I'll *gnaw* you!'

There was a scrabble of claws, a swish and a rat dropped past her eyes. Then another rat thumped onto her shoulder and slid away.

'Right!' said the voice at the back of her neck. 'Now *don't* move, *don't* tread on anyone and keep out of the way!'

'What was *that*?' she hissed, as she felt something slide down her skirt.

'I think it was the one they call Big Savings,' said Keith. 'Here comes the Clan!'

More rats were scrambling into the room, but these moved differently. They stayed together and spread out into a line that moved forward slowly. When an enemy rat attacked it, the line would close up over it quickly, like a fist, and when it opened again that rat was dead.

Only when the surviving rats smelled the terror of their fellows and tried to escape from the room did the attacking line break, become pairs of rats that, with terrible purpose, hunted down one scurrying enemy after another and brought them down with a bite.

And then, seconds after it started, the war was over. The squeaking of a few lucky refugees faded in the walls.

There was a ragged cheer from the Clan rats, the cheer which says 'I'm still alive! After all that!'

2   Turn this extract into playscript and then give a short performance of the scene. You may wish to work alone, in pairs, or in small groups.

Step 1
Consider how many actors you need/have. Remember that you may not need actors for every animal, e.g. the caged rats could be offstage.

Step 2

Highlight the key speeches. You may wish to modify them as you turn them into playscript.

Step 3

Decide on stage directions. Look carefully at how the narrative describes the action and think about how this can be translated on stage, e.g. how the Clan attacks in a straight line initially, then divides into pairs. Also, consider how to convey the impression of rats climbing on Malicia – maybe through her body language, with a voice in her ear 'offstage'?

Step 4

Think about how you can use special effects, e.g. lighting, shadows, music, and background noises, to create an appropriate mood or atmosphere.

Step 5

Allocate parts and begin rehearsing. Share ideas on suitable intonation, expression, and body language to be used by the actors.

Step 6

Stage a performance. After the performance, invite comments from the rest of the class. For example, ask if the action was clear and whether the actors spoke clearly and with conviction. Then consider ways of improving the presentation.

Drama Techniques

Use the following drama techniques to help you to explore the play further.

STILL IMAGE

A still image is like a snapshot of a scene. It captures one moment and holds it still.

Choose one moment in the play where a group of characters are together. Freeze the moment in your mind, then reproduce it as a group 'onstage'. Think carefully about where the actors stand, what they are doing, and their expressions.

Possible scenes for this could be:
- Act 2, Scene 5: Hamnpork's whisper to Darktan, just before he dies
- Act 2, Scene 7: In the Rat King's lair, just after Death has departed
- Act 2, Scene 8: In the town square.

THOUGHT TAPPING

Give each character in your still image (see above) a thought that they are thinking at the moment captured by the image. Ensure that their body language and facial expressions reflect this thought and an appropriate emotion.

IMPROVISATION

Imagine that the 'educated rodents' are being hunted by the rat-catchers. The rodents are hiding in the barn. They need to plan an escape and outwit the rat-catchers, who are just outside. Allocate the roles of Darktan, Nourishing, Hamnpork, Dangerous Beans, Peaches, Sardines, and the two rat-catchers.

All the characters should try to act in role.

Either

1   launch straight into the scene, without any preparation, and see how the action develops

   Or

2   discuss, plan, rehearse, and give a final performance.

If you choose the second option, think about:
- what equipment the rodents have
- what equipment the rat-catchers have
- how each character would react to danger
- who is most likely to have the best ideas
- who is most likely to be best at putting the ideas into action
- how you can introduce some comedy into the scene.

On the Stage

COSTUMES AND PROPS

If an actor is allowed just one item of clothing and one prop to create their character, decide what you would give to:

- Keith
- Malicia
- Peaches
- Dangerous Beans
- Hamnpork
- Darktan

- Sardines
- The Mayor
- Maurice
- Ron
- Bill.

SET DESIGN

1   List the main settings in the play. Choose one of the settings and plan how you would design the set. Think about:
    - the main features it needs to include, e.g. the Rathaus in the town square
    - how many entrances/exits are needed
    - what atmosphere/mood it should convey
    - how you would use colour/decoration to enhance the setting
    - any props essential to the action, e.g. a dresser in Malicia's house, a bench in the town square.

2   Draw a sketch of the setting as you envisage it. Label the essential features.

ILLUSIONS

On a stage it is not always possible to represent things realistically, so you have to be imaginative, to create an illusion. For example, battle scenes can be suggested with just a few characters fighting, but with the addition of background noise to suggest a greater conflict.

1   Can you think of ways of representing
    a)   the rat trap which catches Darktan in Act 2, Scene 2?
    b)   the Rat King and how it is split into individual rats at the end of Act 2, Scene 6?

Think about the use of shadows, lighting, music, sound effects, voices and noises offstage, many actors playing one creature, etc.

● ●

PROGRAMME

Using ICT, design and produce a programme for a performance of 'The Amazing Maurice and his Educated Rodents'. Plan, draft, edit, revise, and proofread your work.

Include:
● a brief outline of the plot (but without giving away the ending!)
● notes on the main characters
● comments on the main issues raised in the play
● short reviews and quotations from critics who have seen previews of the play.

Ideas for Further Activities

1. Carry out some research into Medieval crafts/guilds, their hierarchy, the role they played socially and economically, the symbols for the different guilds, etc.

2. The Rules discussed by Peaches and Dangerous Beans in Act 1, Scene 3, have been written using symbols, rather than words. Look at the illustrations below.

We co-operate, or we die.

Not to Widdle where you Eat.

In the Clan is Strength.

No Rat to Kill Another Rat.

We Are The Changelings.
We Are Not Like Other Rats.

Investigate the history of writing (using the symbols written by Peaches as a starting point). For example, look at hieroglyphics, cuniform, The Rosetta Stone, etc.

3   Examine the Germanic/European 'flavour' of the novel. Look at vocabulary (Bad Blintz, Rathaus, Doppelpunkt, etc.) and description.

4   Geography project: test your mapping skills using the features of the town mentioned in the playscript. Draw up a map, then write directions to certain places.

5   Design and produce a tourist brochure for Bad Blintz, promoting an amazingly rat-friendly town (as proposed by Maurice to the Mayor at the end of the play).